BIBLE FUN FOR TWEENS

Mysteries, Riddles, Puzzles AND MORE

BIBLE FUN FOR TWEENS

Mysteries, Riddles, Puzzles, and More

Writer/Compiler: Marcia Stoner
Designer: Randall Butler
Additional Credits: p. 112

ISBN 978-1-426-70847-3

11 12 13 14 15 16 17 18 19 — 10 9 8 7 6 5 4 3
PACP00534123-03

Manufactured in the United States of America

CONTENTS

How to Use This Book

❊ For arrival or additional activities for any curriculum:

These activities can be used to supplement any Bible curriculum. Use the Topic and Scripture indexes (pp. 108-109, 111) to find the activity that applies to what your tweens are doing.

❊ For a nine-month Bible survey:

If you are doing a school-year overview of the Bible with your tweens, you will find activities for many of the topics you will cover. You would mainly use the activities labeled 1–44 for the first 39 weeks.

❊ For a twelve-month Bible survey:

If you are doing a twelve-month overview of the Bible with your tweens, you will find activities for most of the topics you will cover. The additional summer activities beginning on page 65 may be used in two ways:

1. Strictly for additional topics for summer. (Because so many tweens are in and out of class in the summer months, you probably will not want to leave most of the New Testament work to summer.)

2. At the appropriate place where they fall within the Bible. If you are unsure where that would be, see the Scripture Index on page 111. Those Scriptures with ** preceding them in the index are the additional summer puzzles. They are listed in the index in the order that their Scripture references appear in the Bible.

Creation Through the Prophets

What Did Adam Name Them?

Activity 1

Genesis 2:19-20 tells us that God gave Adam the job of naming the animals. He did a fine job. Can you solve the riddles to discover six of the animals he named?

▲ What has eight legs but cannot walk?

▲ In which animal's name are the first and second letter both the first letter of the alphabet? The last three letters of this name describe the kind of boat Noah built.

▲ What has four pairs of hairy legs to go with its hairy body? Its name rhymes with *spatula.*

▲ What marsupial can hop thirty feet and has a good place to hide money (if it had money)?

▲ What is known for being big and round and is sometimes called a sea elephant?

▲ What long-legged animal is sometimes seen as a plastic pink lawn ornament?

NONE OF THE ANIMALS SHOWN ON THIS PAGE ARE NAMED IN ANY RIDDLE!

Activity 2

Name These Critters

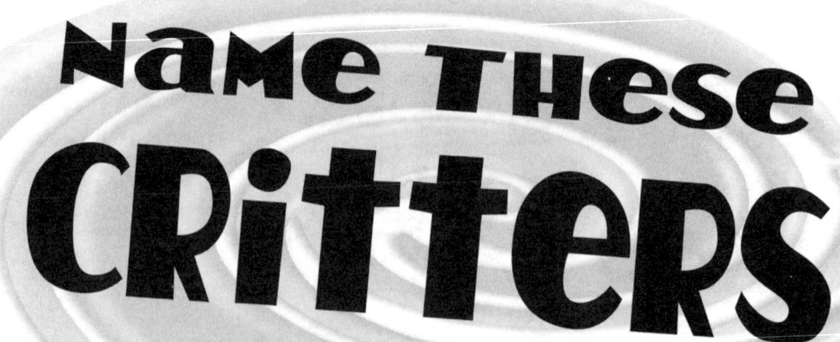

Genesis 2:19-20 tells us that God gave Adam the job of naming the animals. He did a fine job. How would you do? We've mixed up various parts of God's critters to make some unusual ones for you to name. What would you name them? One of these seven critters is real. Can you figure out which one it is?

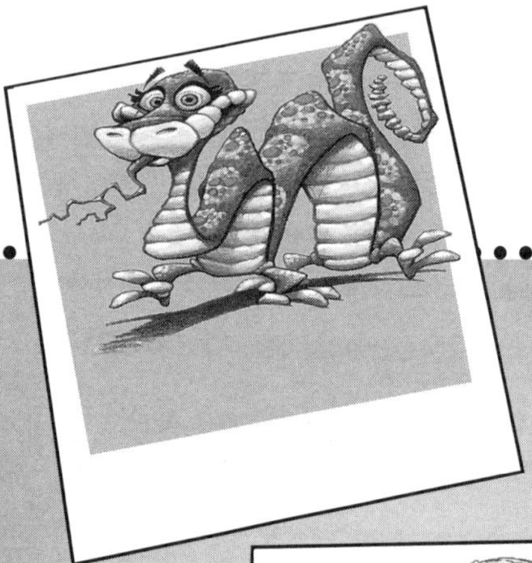

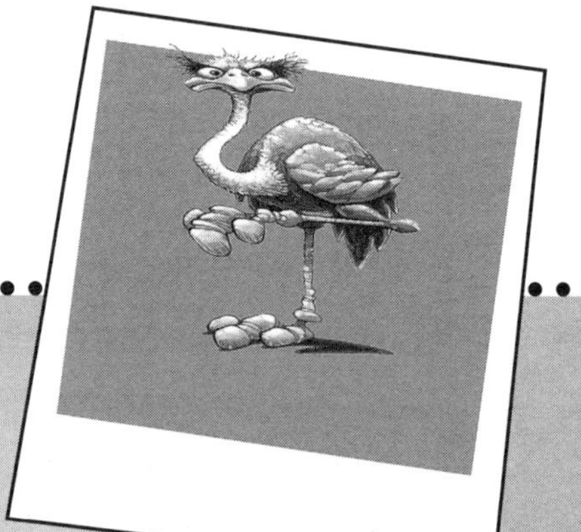

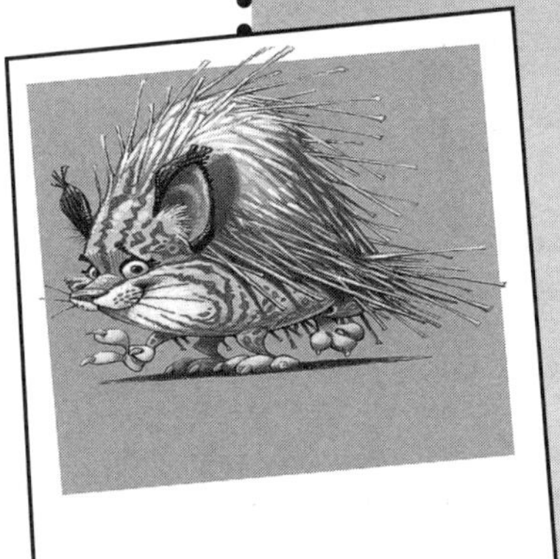

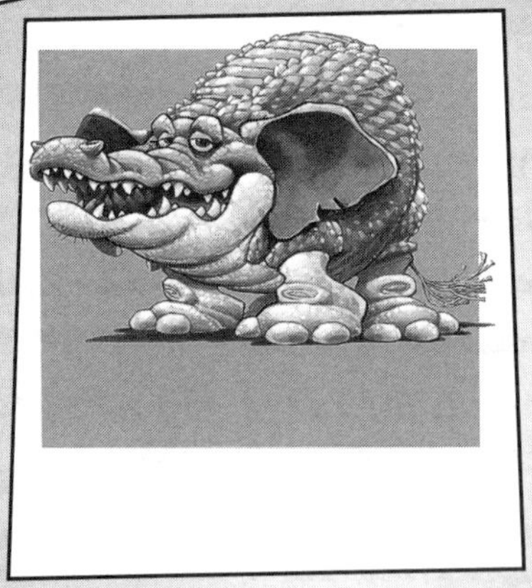

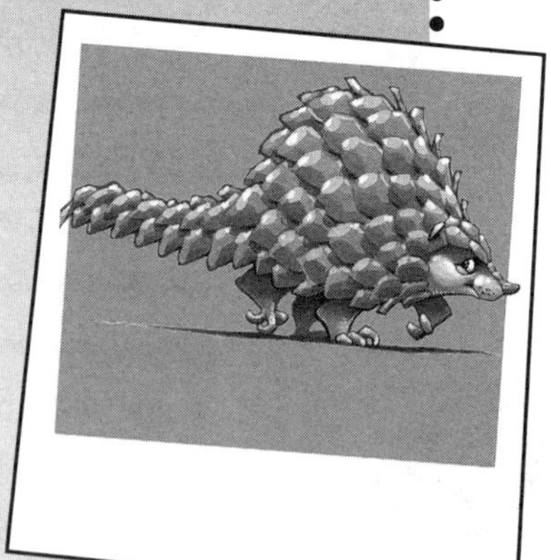

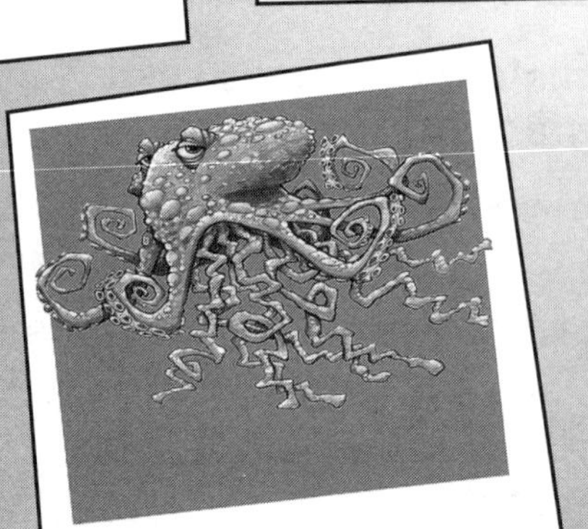

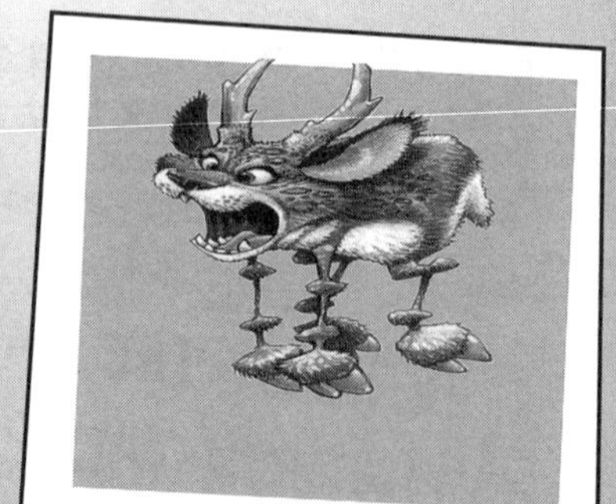

ACTIVITY 3

How many of each clean and unclean animal was Noah supposed to take on the ark? How many birds of the air?

THINK YOU KNOW? BETTER READ GENESIS 7:2-3.

ONE CUBIT IS ABOUT EIGHTEEN INCHES. THERE ARE TWELVE INCHES IN A FOOT.

WHAT CREATURES WERE NOT ON THE ARK WHEN THE FLOOD CAME?

Genesis 6:15 says of the ark: "This is how you are to make it: the length of the ark three hundred cubits, its width fifty cubits, and its height thirty cubits."

HOW LONG, HOW WIDE, AND HOW HIGH WAS THE ARK IN FEET?

ACTIVITY 4 — OLDER THAN METHUSELAH?

There's an old saying, "He's older than Methuselah." (It's sort of like saying someone is older than dirt. No one's really older than dirt.) According to the Bible, Methuselah lived longer than any other person. Can you figure out how old these people lived to be?

HINT: YOU'LL NEED TO FIGURE OUT ADAM'S AGE FIRST.

- ▲ **ADAM:** 1800 ÷ 2 + 60 – 30 = ___________ years old.
- ▲ **SETH:** Subtract 18 from Adam's age = ___________ years old.
- ▲ **ENOSH:** Subtract 7 from Seth's age = ___________ years old.
- ▲ **KENAN:** Add 5 to Enosh's age = ___________ years old.
- ▲ **MAHALALEL:** Subtract 15 from Kenan's age = ___________ years old.
- ▲ **JARED:** Add 67 to Mahalalel's age = ___________ years old.
- ▲ **ENOCH:** Subtract 597 from Jared's age = ___________ years old.
  (Hint: equals number of days in a year.)
- ▲ **METHUSELAH:** Add 604 to Enoch's age = ___________ years old.
- ▲ **LAMECH:** Subtract 192 from Methuselah's age = ___________ years old.
  (Hint: all three digits are the same.)
- ▲ **NOAH:** Add 173 years to Lamech's age = ___________ years old.

Now can you figure out how old Abraham and Sarah were when their son Isaac was born?

Abraham was exactly one century old when Isaac was born.
___________ years old.
Sarah was 90 when Isaac was conceived. So how old was she probably when he was born? ___________ years old.

CAN'T FIGURE IT OUT? SEE GENESIS 5:5, 8, 11, 14, 17, 20, 23, 27, 31; 9:29; 17:17; 21:5.

He was Tricky

Activity 5

Rebekah and Isaac had only two sons. They were named Jacob and Esau. What was the name of Jacob's twin?

Jacob was always trying to get ahead, even before he was born.

Unscramble these two words to discover what his name means.

LEHE RBEGABR

Jacob's name was changed by God. Use the code below to discover what it was changed to.

A
B
C
D
E
F
G
H
I
J
K
L
M
N
O
P
Q
R
S

Jacob tricked his brother. Which of the following do you think is the trick he most likely played on Esau?

He short-sheeted his bed.
He threw a fake snake at him.
He got him to trade his inheritance for a bowl of soup.
He figured out a way to get the best of his sheep. (Sheep were very valuable.)
He tricked him into marrying the wrong woman.
He got him to sit on a whoopee cushion.

HINTS:

Jacob played one of these tricks on Esau.
Jacob played one of these tricks on his father-in-law, Laban.
One of these tricks was played on Jacob.
The other three didn't happen.

NEED HELP? LOOK AT GENESIS 25:24-26, 25:29-35, 29:18-25, 30:25-43, 32:27-28

THE MYSTERY OF THE DREAMS

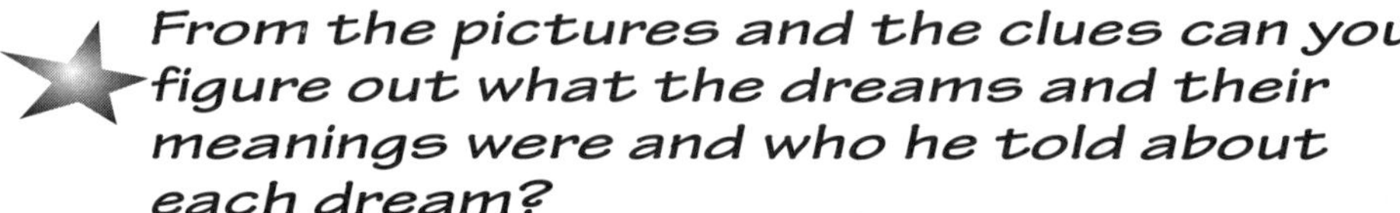

Joseph was known both for his own dreams and for interpreting the dreams of others. (He was given the interpretations by God.)

From the pictures and the clues can you figure out what the dreams and their meanings were and who he told about each dream?

JOSEPH'S OWN DREAMS (GENESIS 37:5-11)

Jacob was Joseph's father. Rachel was Joseph's mother. Jacob had twelve sons.

Joseph dreamed that his brothers' sheaves of grain bowed down to his sheaf of grain.

Joseph dreamed that the sun, the moon, and the stars bowed down to him.

One man dreamed there were three baskets of bread and the birds were eating out of the one on top. Joseph said this meant that the dreamer would be dead in three days.

Pharaoh dreamed of things in groups of sevens.

Pharaoh's cupbearer dreamed of pressing grapes into Pharaoh's cup and then placing the cup in Pharaoh's hand.

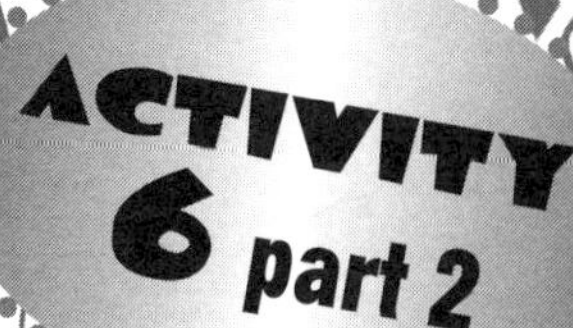

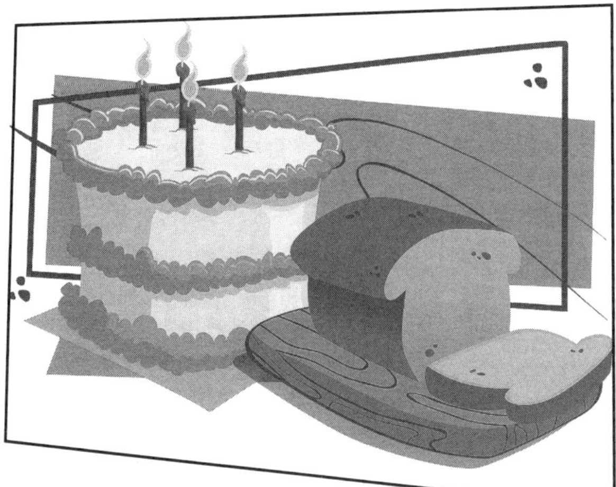

Pharaoh's chief baker dreamed about his work.

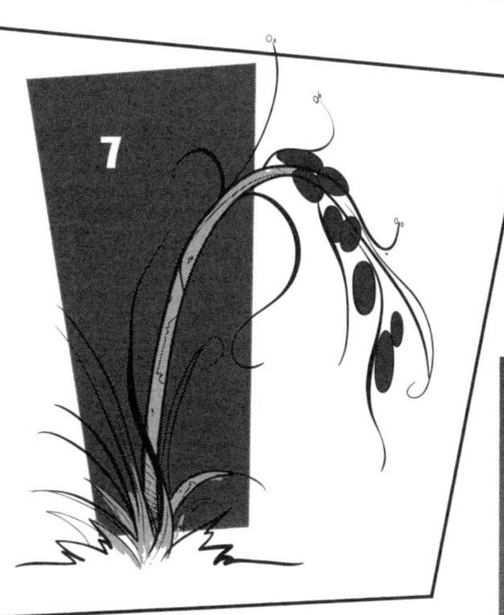

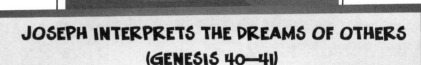

JOSEPH INTERPRETS THE DREAMS OF OTHERS (GENESIS 40–41)

While in jail Joseph met Pharaoh's chief baker and chief cupbearer.

Joseph said there would be seven good years with plenty of food and then seven years of drought.

Evidently dreaming about the cup meant the person handing it to Pharaoh would soon be serving Pharaoh again.

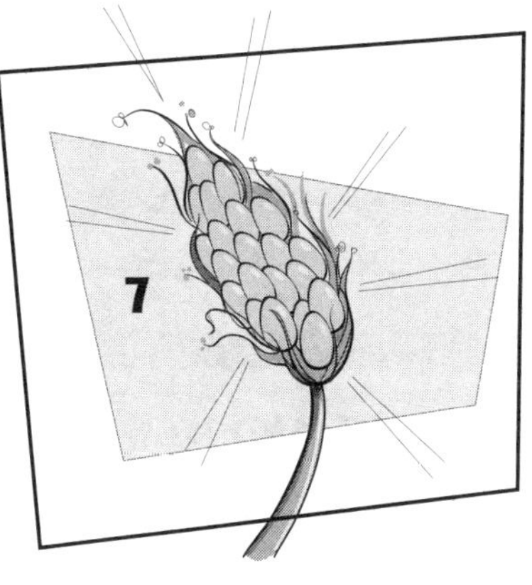

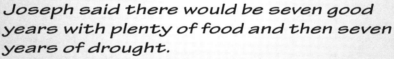

When Joseph was young he was always bragging to his brothers. They didn't like it very much.

In a biblical dream bowing means the person being bowed down to is destined for greatness.

It took ten plagues for Pharaoh to let the Israelites go. Find the plagues in the word search. Then follow the clues to number them in order.

Ten Plagues

D	Y	G	J	M	B	W	P	O	U	N	C	L	T	S	A	J	Y
J	E	Z	E	C	D	E	A	W	S	W	E	D	T	H	V	P	K
R	N	A	L	N	O	S	Z	E	G	Q	U	I	M	L	N	K	K
N	I	G	T	P	B	S	N	T	O	V	Y	J	S	D	A	Z	N
Z	O	R	T	H	U	N	D	E	R	A	N	D	H	A	I	L	I
A	D	A	A	L	O	D	V	K	F	R	E	N	Q	U	M	B	G
N	E	D	C	M	B	F	G	N	Z	A	U	T	Y	E	P	S	S
P	R	L	D	O	P	Z	F	L	I	E	S	W	D	N	I	T	T
P	U	I	E	H	Z	S	L	I	O	B	Y	M	A	C	A	S	O
E	Q	U	S	P	E	I	O	H	R	J	E	Z	A	N	E	U	J
L	V	Q	A	J	U	D	Q	U	J	S	R	M	G	O	V	C	M
W	A	T	E	R	T	U	R	N	E	D	T	O	B	L	O	O	D
K	B	S	S	E	N	K	R	A	D	O	C	B	L	O	B	L	Y
B	E	Y	I	S	V	E	Y	B	Z	V	I	D	O	N	E	R	S
W	I	R	D	O	D	A	Y	I	C	M	U	T	A	R	M	E	T
W	K	E	D	M	B	O	Z	R	Y	I	V	U	A	Y	N	G	W

◯ BOILS
◯ DARKNESS
◯ DEATH OF FIRSTBORN
◯ DISEASED CATTLE
◯ FLIES
◯ FROGS
◯ GNATS
◯ LOCUSTS
◯ THUNDER AND HAIL
◯ WATER TURNED TO BLOOD

Plague #1—bad for fish.
Plague #2—involves things that hop
Plague #3—nasty little bugs that bite
Plague #4—things we swat
Plague #5—means no hamburgers
Plague #6—sores on the body
Plague #7—means bad storms are coming
Plague #8—long-legged bugs that eat everything in sight
Plague #9—would cause use of a lot of flashlights
Plague #10—is the worst plague

WHO DID WHAT?

ACTIVITY 8

Can you draw one continuous line connecting all the things about Joshua and one continuous line connecting all the things about Moses without the two lines crossing?

- ▲ Was told to remove his sandals because he was standing on holy ground.
- ▲ Sent spies into the Promised Land.
- ▲ Wandered in the wilderness for forty years.
- ▲ Led the people out of Egypt.
- ▲ Gave God's law to the Israelite people.
- ▲ Was given specific directions by God on how to lead the people.
- ▲ Was called by God.
- ▲ Was assured by God that God would be with him.
- ▲ Led the people into the Promised Land.
- ▲ Proclaimed God's law to the people of Israel.

BIBLE HELPS:

EXODUS 3, 12, 24:13, 34:32;
NUMBERS 13:1–14:24;
JOSHUA 1–4; 5:15; 23

Activity 9

A Theft at the Gallery

There was a theft at the Bible Gallery of Art last night. The thief made off with one of the portraits from one wall in the Bible Women of Fame section. Not only that, but he took all of the name plates off the wall so that Detective Whosit doesn't even know for sure which portrait is missing.

- Can you follow the clues to match each woman's name with her portrait? Then can you help Detective Whosit figure out whose portrait is missing and who the thief is?

- Detective Whosit suspects that the name plates were taken because the thief is associated in some way with the person in the missing portrait.

- Detective Whosit interviewed the guard, the art gallery's director (who is also a Bible scholar), the receptionist, and a frequent visitor to the art gallery.

WE HAVE NUMBERED THE PORTRAITS TO MAKE IT EASIER FOR YOU.

1

2

3

4

After interviewing witnesses, Detective Whosit returned to the police station, where he searched the computer records and discovered that Eve has a police record. She was caught pilfering fruit from a protected area. He also discovered that Deborah was a famous judge. That's bad for the culprit if it's her portrait. Stealing the portrait of a judge could get you forty years in the slammer.

Detective Whosit also went over his notes from the witness interviews at the gallery:

- The guard says he always thought Sarah was too old to have a baby.

NOTE: WHY WOULD THE GUARD SAY THAT?

- The receptionist says that it's rumored that Rebekah hung out at the local well. The rumor goes that Rebekah claimed to be getting water to give to the animals.
- The gallery director (a well-known Bible scholar) claimed that Esther was a queen and was known for her beautiful clothing and jewelry. He also knew a lot about Ruth, stating she was known for gleaning from fields. Everybody knows you have to do something with all that raw grain. So it's probably true that Ruth baked a great loaf of bread.
- The gallery visitor said she was always drawn to the portrait of Chloe, who was an important woman in the church at Corinth. The visitor says she read somewhere that the meaning of Chloe's name is "blonde."

Detective Whosit also had the witnesses come to the station to look at mug shots.

The men below were all identified as having visited the gallery the day of the theft.

THIS IS WHAT DETECTIVE WHOSIT DISCOVERED ABOUT EACH MAN AS HE INTERVIEWED THE SUSPECTS AND THEIR RELATIVES.

BOAZ—He's always had a thing for the woman who came to glean in his fields. In fact, he married her.

ABRAHAM—His son Isaac claims that his dad always wanted the portrait of Sarah with baby Isaac to hang over his mantel.

HAMAN—He doesn't like the queen; she takes Mordecai's side in every argument, and the king likes her better than Haman. Haman has always wanted to destroy her portrait.

ADAM—He thinks Eve's portrait hanging in the gallery might draw too much attention. He doesn't want the authorities to come after them. He still cringes when people talk about fruit.

BARAK—He won't go anywhere without the judge at his side.

ISAAC—His father sent a servant to find him a wife. The servant was directed by God to a well where a young woman would come to draw water.

HAVE YOU FIGURED OUT WHOSE PORTRAIT IS MISSING AND WHO THE THIEF IS?

ACTIVITY 10

Saul Tangram

Cut the shapes apart and see how quickly you can arrange them in the outline to complete the picture of Saul.

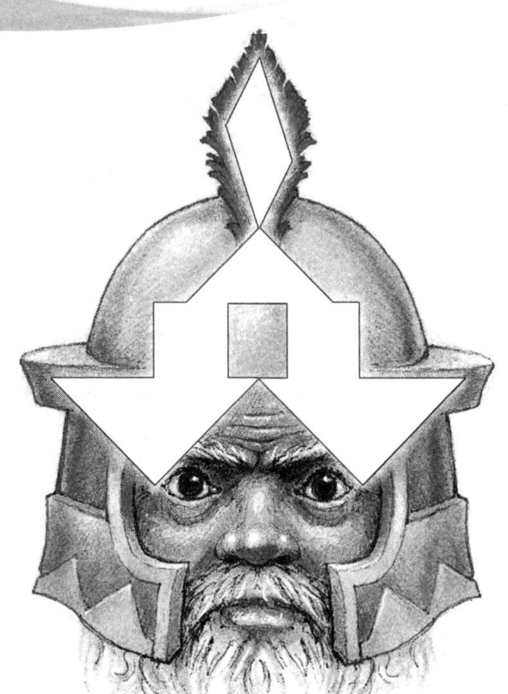

ACTIVITY 11

The Case of the Missing Vowels

Somebody stole all the vowels from this Bible verse. Can you supply the missing vowels and figure out what Proverbs 3:5 says?

TR__ST __N TH__ L__RD W__TH __LL Y__ __R

H__ __RT, __ND D__ N__T R__LY __N

Y__ __R __WN __NS__GHT.

TO MAKE IT EASIER WE AREN'T USING Y AS A VOWEL.

ARK OF THE COVENANT MYSTERIOUSLY DISAPPEARS

Indiana Jones made false claims that he found the true ark of the covenant. He doesn't even seem to know everything that was inside of it. The ark did mysteriously disappear centuries ago, and people are still looking for it. Can you figure out what it holds and where it is now?

SOME OF THE BUILDING PLANS ARE SCRAMBLED. CAN YOU FIGURE THEM OUT?

PEOPLE ASSOCIATED WITH THE ARK

Moses, Aaron, Joshua, priests, Samuel, Philistines, David, Uzzah, Solomon Jeremiah, Queen of Sheba

BUILDING PLANS

- They shall make an ark of aaaicc dowo.
- It shall be 2½ buitcs long, 1½ wide, and 1½ high.
- Overlay it with pure logd, edinsi and edotusi.
- Cast _____ rings of gold for it and put them on its _____ feet. (The number of rings = 2 + 2; the number of feet is the same as the number of rings.)
- Make poles of aaaicc dowo and overlay them with logd.
- Make a ecrmy teas of pure logd and make two mcherubi, one for each end.

(Need help? See Exodus 25:10-19)

WHO TOOK THE ARK THE FIRST TIME? SEE I SAMUEL 4

HISTORY: THE BEGINNING

The leader of people wandering in wilderness (he had led them out of Egypt) was given building plans for the ark. (Exodus 25:1, 10–15)

The rod used by Moses' brother was put in the ark of the covenant. (Numbers 17:8-10)

The man who led the people into the Promised Land asked these religious people to carry the ark over the Jordan River. (Joshua 3:6)

The ark was captured in battle by the enemies of Israel. (1 Samuel 4)

When the ark was brought in on a cart, a man reached out a hand to steady it. He was struck dead for not handling the ark with reverence. (2 Samuel 6:6)

There was much dancing and celebration when the king had the ark brought into Jerusalem. (2 Samuel 6:5)

The son of David built the Temple and placed the ark in the Holy of Holies. (1 Kings 8:1-9)

David danced before the ark.
Solomon was David's son.
Moses led the people out of Egypt.
God gave the people manna to eat in the wilderness.
Aaron was Moses' brother.
Joshua led the people into the Promised Land.

WHAT'S REALLY IN THE ARK?

The stone tablets Moses brought down from the mountain. On them were written some "shalls" and "shall nots."

WHAT WAS ON THE TABLETS?

Moses' brother had a special rod that was placed in the ark. It is said to have budded to show the people that God had chosen Moses.

WHOSE NAME WAS GIVEN TO THE ROD?

A golden urn of the stuff the Israelites ate while wandering in the wilderness.

WHAT WAS IN THE GOLDEN URN?

Hebrews 9:4-5

▲ WHO MADE SURE THE ARK WAS CARRIED INTO THE PROMISED LAND?

▲ WHO BROUGHT THE ARK INTO JERUSALEM?

▲ WHO PUT THE ARK IN THE TEMPLE?

587 B.C.

BABYLONIANS DESTROY TEMPLE.

Ark of the covenant disappears.

Story on page 7.

Indiana Jones didn't really find the ark. So where is it now?

THEORY 1:

Sheba was a place that colonized some parts of Africa, including Ethiopia. The queen of Sheba grew rich through trade.

Christian Ethiopians claim that when the queen of Sheba visited King Solomon she took the ark of the covenant back to Ethiopia, where to this day it is guarded by a monk who cannot step outside of the chapel grounds.

No one but the monk sees the ark.

If it's there, why won't they let anyone see it?

Read about the queen of Sheba in 1 Kings 10:1-13 and 2 Chronicles 9:1-12

THEORY 2:

The prophet Jeremiah lived at the time that the Babylonians destroyed the Temple and carried the Israelites into captivity.

One tradition says that Jeremiah took the ark of the covenant and hid it in a cave to keep it out of the hands of the Babylonians.

If that is what happened, he must have hidden it well. Nobody has ever found it.

THEORY 3:

It is said that the prophet Jeremiah was commissioned to take King Zedekiah's daughter to Ireland to marry the king there.

It is said that Jeremiah also took the ark of the covenant with him to Ireland.

It is also claimed that Jeremiah is buried in Ireland.

Could these things be true?

WHERE DO YOU THINK THE ARK OF THE COVENANT IS?

ACTIVITY 13

The Holy of Holies

Can you enter the Temple and get to the Holy of Holies?

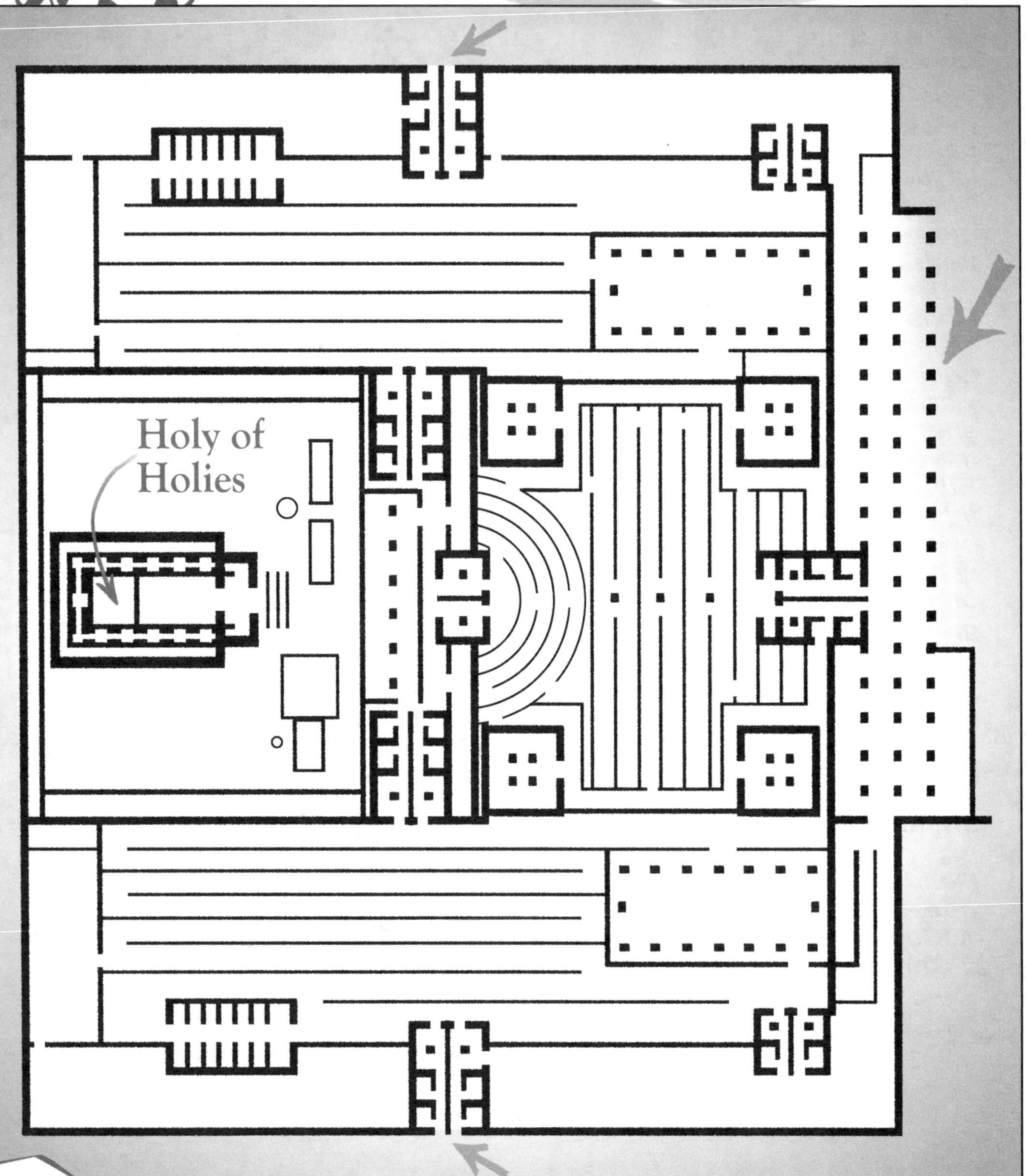

Most Didn't Do It

Hidden Message

Find the kings listed below in the word search. When you have found them all, read the leftover letters from left to right, starting at the top row, to discover some advice that the kings of the Divided Kingdom should have paid attention to. Some did. Most didn't. (You can check your answer in Luke 11:28, though this isn't the first time such advice was given.)

- ABIJAM
- AHAB
- AHAZIAH
- AMAZIAH
- ASA
- BAASHA
- HOSHEA
- JEHOAHAZ
- JEHOSHAPHAT
- JOASH
- JOTHAM
- JEROBOAM
- OMRI
- REHOBOAM
- SHALLUM
- ZIMRI

B	L	E	J	E	H	O	S	H	A	P	H	A	T	S
H	S	A	M	A	Z	I	A	H	E	D	R	A	T	J
O	H	A	S	A	H	E	Z	R	Z	I	M	R	I	E
S	A	R	E	S	T	A	H	A	H	S	A	A	B	R
H	O	S	A	E	H	W	S	H	A	L	L	U	M	O
E	H	O	O	A	H	E	A	O	M	R	I	R	T	B
A	J	H	O	E	W	A	H	A	Z	I	A	H	O	O
R	D	H	J	O	T	H	A	M	O	F	G	O	D	A
A	E	N	D	A	B	I	J	A	M	O	B	E	Y	M
J	I	R	E	H	O	B	O	A	M	T	A	H	A	B

ACTIVITY 15

Mortal Enemies

Isaiah tells us that when the Messiah comes, peace will reign on the earth. One sign of this is that animals that are normally mortal enemies will learn to live together in peace. Follow the clues to match the animals in Isaiah 11:6-8.

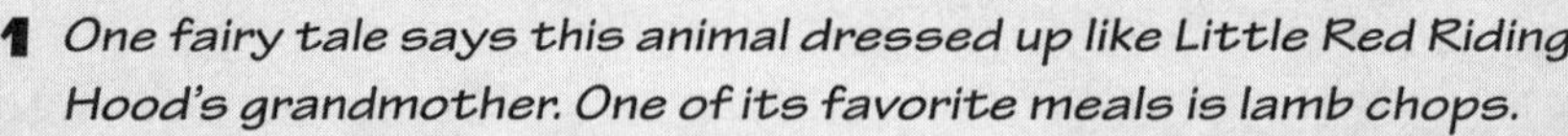

1 *One fairy tale says this animal dressed up like Little Red Riding Hood's grandmother. One of its favorite meals is lamb chops.*

2 *In the nursery rhyme Mary had one of these (it was little), and it followed her to school. To the question, "Who's afraid of the big bad wolf?" this animal would reply, "I am."*

3 *It is said that this animal will eat anything, including tin cans. Some of them have beards. A baby one is called a "kid."*

4 *This animal is known for running real fast. People also say it "can't change its spots." It can outrun little tin-can eaters.*

5 *This animal is really a baby cow or a baby bull. In the peaceable kingdom it gets along with two other animals.*

6 *This animal likes to roar, especially at baby animals. But in the peaceable kingdom it will get along with two other animals.*

7 *Of these two animals, one likes to sleep all winter and the other chews its cud. In the peaceable kingdom they will graze together.*

8 *This animal is very strong and is often used to pull large heavy loads.*

9 *This animal was roaring earlier and has already been matched with two other animals, but in the peaceable kingdom, this king of the jungle will also eat straw with the strong puller of heavy loads.*

10 *Mothers usually don't like it when children play with these creatures that slither.*

NOTE: A fatling is a cow, goat, or other animal that has grown.

IF YOU WANT TO KNOW WHO'S GOING TO LEAD THEM ALL, READ ISAIAH 11:6.

Can you think of another set of animals that would be mortal enemies? Think up clues to identify them.

NEW TESTAMENT

Mysteries, Riddles, Puzzles AND MORE

PART I

Advent Through the Transfiguration

The Reason for the Season

ACTIVITY 16

Advent and Christmas are a time to celebrate the birth of the Messiah, Jesus the Christ. Among all the decorations for the season can you find the Christian symbols?

HOLIDAY DECOR

Activity 17

The Baby Album

While rummaging through the attic one day, LaErica came upon a photo album in an old trunk. The album was old and dusty and was filled with photographs of babies. When she opened it up, several of the photos fell out. The album is crumbling, and LaErica wants to reconstruct it by putting the pictures in the correct order in a new photo album she has purchased.

There are also several old documents in the trunk. You've been invited over to help LaErica reconstruct the album. Can you help her out?

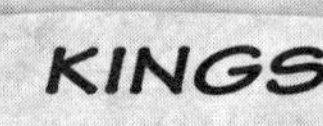

Saul: 1020-1000
David: 1000-961
Solomon: 961-928
Rehoboam: 922-915 (Judah)
Jeroboam: 922-901 (Israel)

David is not pictured, but his son is.

Jacob had a twin brother named Esau.

No pictures of Abraham were ever in existence.

Inscription on back of this photo says "Obed, son of Ruth, the grain gatherer." ←

Family Tree

Abraham	Sarah
Isaac	Rebekah
Jacob	Rachel

Joseph

Boaz	Ruth

Obed
Jesse
David
Solomon

Baptism Certificate

This designates that

____

has been baptized.

John

ACTIVITY 17 part 3

It's a good thing God showed Abraham that ram in a thicket or Isaac might have been sacrificed as a young boy. (Genesis 22)

Joseph, a son of Jacob, brought his brothers to Egypt so they wouldn't starve. (Genesis 42–50)

Eventually the Israelites became slaves. They needed someone to lead them out of Egypt. That person was Moses. As a baby Moses was placed in the reeds in the Nile River to protect him. (Exodus 1–3)

Samuel anoints David with oil, making him king of Israel. (1 Samuel 16:13)

John the Baptist grows up to baptize his cousin Jesus. John was born just six months before Jesus. Read his story in the Gospels. (Luke 1; Matthew 3:13-17)

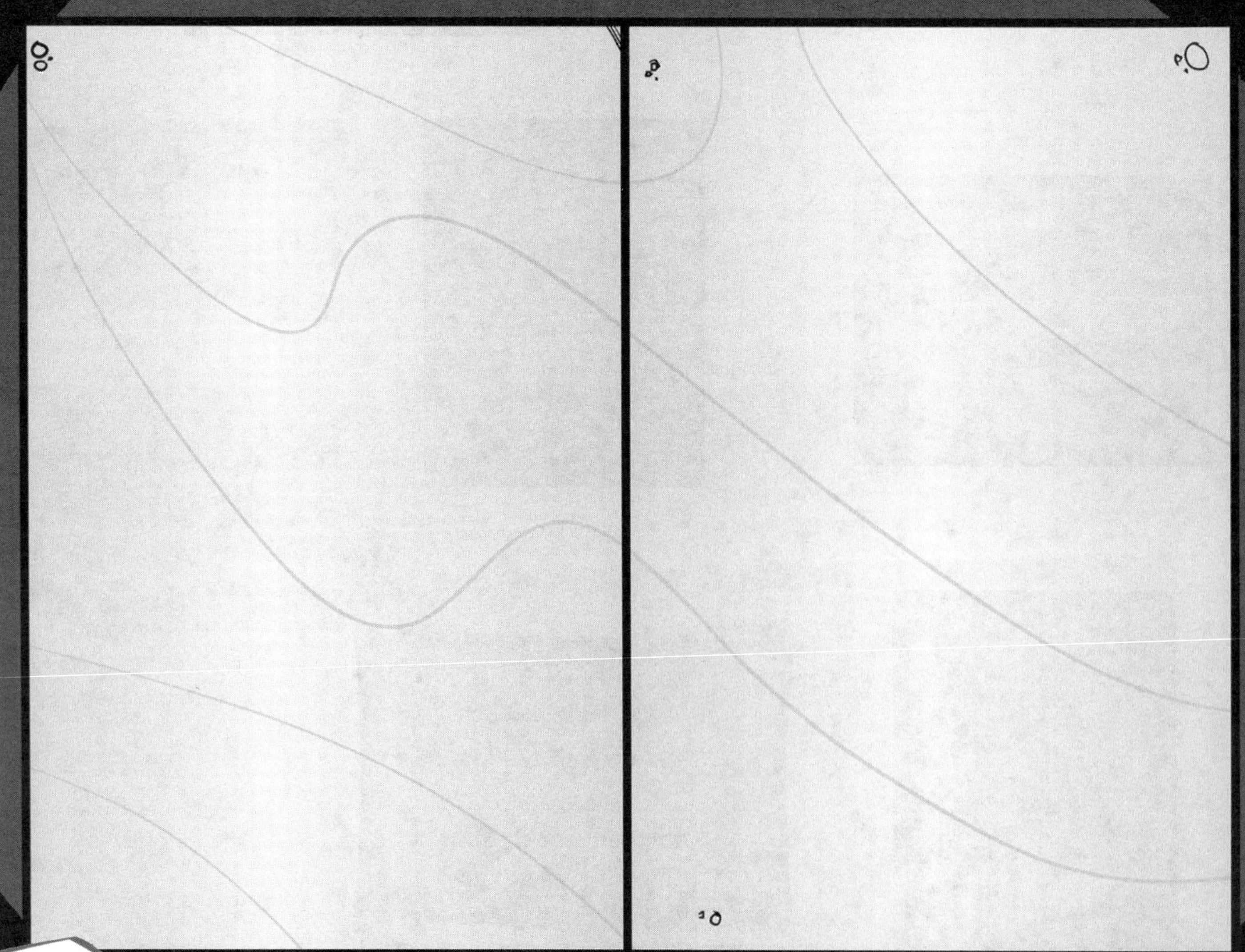

Census Forms

Activity 18

In those days a decree went out from Emperor Augustus that all the world should be registered. (Luke 2:1)

To be registered means that a census was taken. A census is usually for reasons of deciding who's going to be taxed.

We've gathered some census forms from this census. The names are missing. Can you figure out whose they might be?

Not all of these people would have been from Bethlehem. *(See the list of registrants on p. 34.)*

- **NAME:** ____________________
- **OCCUPATION:**
  - ____ farmer / animal caregiver
  - ____ government official
  - ____ astrologer
  - ____ construction worker / furniture maker
  - _X_ priest / prophet
  - ____ hotel industry
- **INCOME:**
  - ____ very little but food and shelter
  - ____ I make a living
  - ____ pretty much middle class
  - _X_ good money
  - ____ rich
- **REASON FOR REGISTERING HERE:**
  - ____ hometown
  - ____ this is where I work
  - ____ traveling / return trip would take too long
  - _X_ other:
    six-month-old son, can't travel

BIBLE REFERENCE: LUKE 1

- **NAME:** ____________________
- **OCCUPATION:**
  - ____ farmer / animal caregiver
  - ____ government official
  - ____ astrologer
  - _X_ construction worker / furniture maker
  - ____ priest / prophet
  - ____ hotel industry
- **INCOME:**
  - ____ very little but food and shelter
  - _X_ I make a living
  - ____ pretty much middle class
  - ____ good money
  - ____ rich
- **REASON FOR REGISTERING HERE:**
  - _X_ hometown
  - ____ this is where I work
  - ____ traveling / return trip would take too long
  - _X_ other:
    also fulfills Scripture

BIBLE REFERENCE: LUKE 2

- **NAME:** ______________________

- **OCCUPATION:**
  - ___ farmer / animal caregiver
  - _X_ government official
  - ___ astrologer
  - ___ construction worker / furniture maker
  - ___ priest / prophet
  - ___ hotel industry

- **INCOME:**
  - ___ very little but food and shelter
  - ___ I make a living
  - ___ pretty much middle class
  - ___ good money
  - _X_ rich

- **REASON FOR REGISTERING HERE:**
  - ___ hometown
  - _X_ this is where I work
  - ___ traveling / return trip would take too long
  - ___ other:

BIBLE REFERENCE: MATTHEW 2

- **NAME:** ______________________

- **OCCUPATION:**
  - ___ farmer / animal caregiver
  - ___ government official
  - _X_ astrologer
  - ___ construction worker / furniture maker
  - ___ priest / prophet
  - ___ hotel industry

- **INCOME:**
  - ___ very little but food and shelter
  - ___ I make a living
  - ___ pretty much middle class
  - _X_ good money
  - ___ rich

- **REASON FOR REGISTERING HERE:**
  - ___ hometown
  - ___ this is where I work
  - _X_ traveling / return trip would take too long
  - ___ other:

BIBLE REFERENCE: MATTHEW 2

List of Registrants

King Herod
innkeeper
Joseph of Nazareth
shepherd
wise man
Zechariah

- **NAME:** ____________________
- **OCCUPATION:**
  - ___ farmer / animal caregiver
  - ___ government official
  - ___ astrologer
  - ___ construction worker / furniture maker
  - ___ priest / prophet
  - _X_ hotel industry
- **INCOME:**
  - ___ very little but food and shelter
  - ___ I make a living
  - _X_ pretty much middle class
  - ___ good money
  - ___ rich
- **REASON FOR REGISTERING HERE:**
  - ___ hometown
  - _X_ this is where I work
  - ___ traveling / return trip would take too long
  - ___ other:

BIBLE REFERENCE: LUKE 2

- **NAME:** ____________________
- **OCCUPATION:**
  - _X_ farmer / animal caregiver
  - ___ government official
  - ___ astrologer
  - ___ construction worker / furniture maker
  - ___ priest / prophet
  - ___ hotel industry
- **INCOME:**
  - _X_ very little but food and shelter
  - ___ I make a living
  - ___ pretty much middle class
  - ___ good money
  - ___ rich
- **REASON FOR REGISTERING HERE:**
  - ___ hometown
  - ___ this is where I work
  - ___ traveling / return trip would take too long
  - _X_ other:

    was told to come here

BIBLE REFERENCE: LUKE 2

ACTIVITY 19

MORE GIFTS?

If you read Matthew 2, you will discover that the Bible does not tell us how many wise men there were. It just tells us there were three gifts.

The number of wise men is part of the tradition of western Christianity and it's based upon the number of gifts. However, the eastern tradition says there were twelve wise men. Gold, frankincense, and myrrh were expensive gifts. Maybe some of the wise men went together to buy these gifts? And what if a few of the other wise men brought gifts, but they weren't as memorable as the gifts mentioned in the Bible?

Find the words indicated in the Scriptures listed below to discover what other gifts would have been appropriate for a first-century baby.

EXODUS 27:20, WORD 14

LUKE 9:3, LAST WORD

PSALM 132:17, WORD 16

LUKE 2:7, WORDS 13 THROUGH 15

Three Things

What do these three objects have in common?

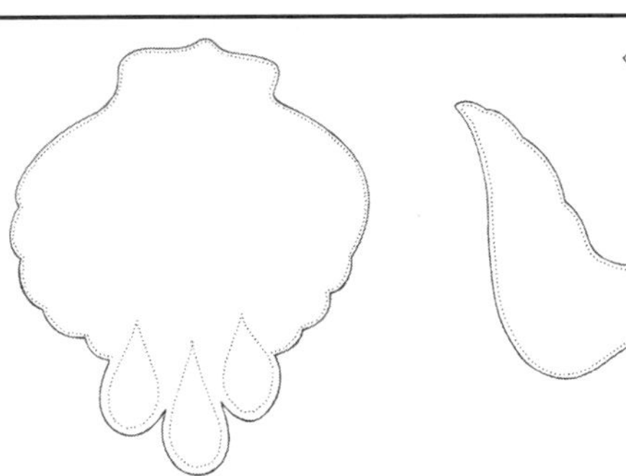

As Easy as 1, 2, 3

To decipher the message below figure out which missing vowel each of the numbers below stands for. Then fill in the Scripture verse to discover John's declaration.

___ mys___lf hav___ s______n and hav___
1 2 2 2 2 2

t___st___f______d that th___s ___s th___
2 1 1 2 1 1 2

S___n ___f G___d. John 1:34
3 3 3

vowels = a, e, i, o u (and sometimes y)

ACTIVITY 22

The Message

Follow the arrows from box to box. Boxes connected by arrows share the same letter. You will discover what Jesus said at the beginning of his ministry. (Luke 4:18)

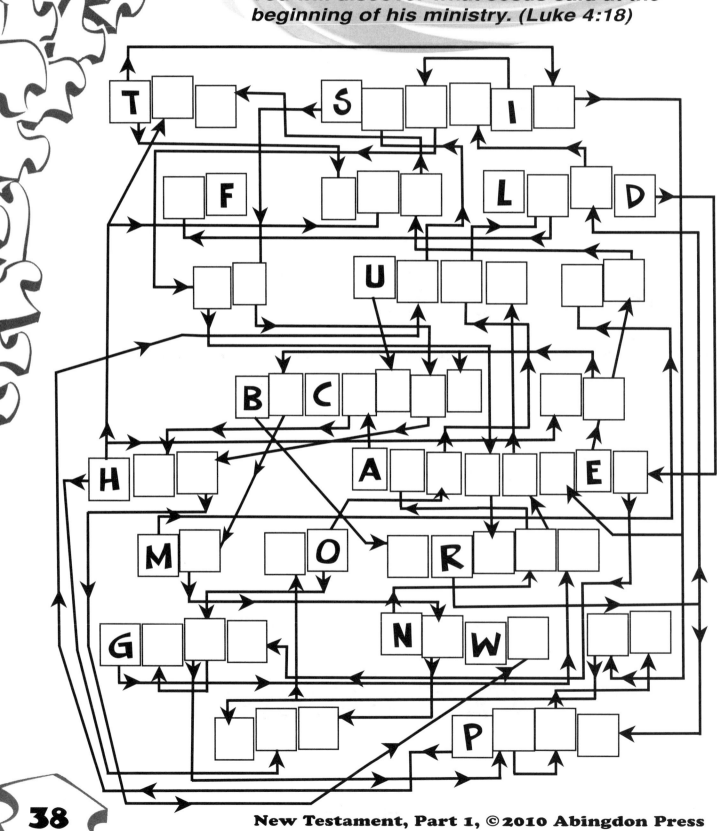

T S I F L D U B C A E H M O R N W G P

First Disciples

ACTIVITY 23

Someone has taken the names of Jesus' first disciples and switched out the first letters of their names. (If more than one word to a name, the last part of the name has the same problem.)

Can you figure out all the names correctly? Use the clues in part two to help you if you need it.

* ZAMES
* PNDREW
* JARTHOLOMEW
* MOHN
* WETER
* JATTHEW
* JHOMAS
* TAMES SON OF ILPHAEUS
* BUDAS ASCARIOT
* AUDAS SON OF PAMES
* TIMON THE TEALOT
* SHILIP

Hints to some of the disciples' true names are in the ten sentences below.

1. Simple Simon met a pie man going to the fair.
2. Someone who is really, really enthusiastic about a cause is called a "zealot."
3. Julie Andrews was the star of the movie *The Sound of Music*.
4. Peter, Peter, pumpkin eater, how does your garden grow?
5. Audas and Budas really should have the same first letter in common.
6. Alphabet, alpaca, and Alps are nice words.
7. The letter J in the list of disciples' names is always followed by a vowel.
8. SHILIP should begin and end with the same letter.
9. The four Gospels are Matthew, Mark, Luke, and John.
10. You could look these names up in Luke 6:12-16.

A certain person is called to be a disciple. Can you figure out who it is?

▲ ***It's a person you are with every day (no exceptions). It's the only person who knows every secret you have.***

Who calls modern disciples?

▲ ***It's someone who is with you every day (no exceptions), someone who knows every secret you have.***

Backward Beatitudes

Activity 24

A mirror might be handy for reading the Beatitudes (Matthew 5:3-12a).

- Blessed are the poor in spirit, for theirs is the kingdom of heaven.
- Blessed are those who mourn, for they will be comforted.
- Blessed are the meek, for they will inherit the earth.
- Blessed are those who hunger and thirst for righteousness, for they will be filled.
- Blessed are the merciful, for they will receive mercy.
- Blessed are the pure in heart, for they will see God.
- Blessed are the peacemakers, for they will be called children of God.
- Blessed are those who are persecuted for righteousness' sake, for theirs is the kingdom of heaven.
- Blessed are you when people revile you and persecute you and utter all kinds of evil against you falsely on my account. Rejoice and be glad, for your reward is great in heaven.

House Hunting

Irving wants to buy a house. He prefers an ocean view. He has seen two ads and looked up the houses on the Internet. Which house should he buy?

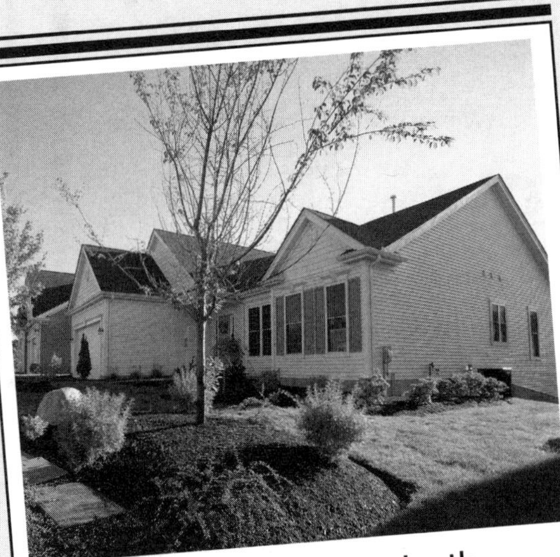

Three-bedroom, two-bath house right on the beach. Great view. Large open kitchen with all the latest stainless steel appliances. Open floor plan. Large deck. Two-car garage. Foundation built on sand to be environmentally friendly.

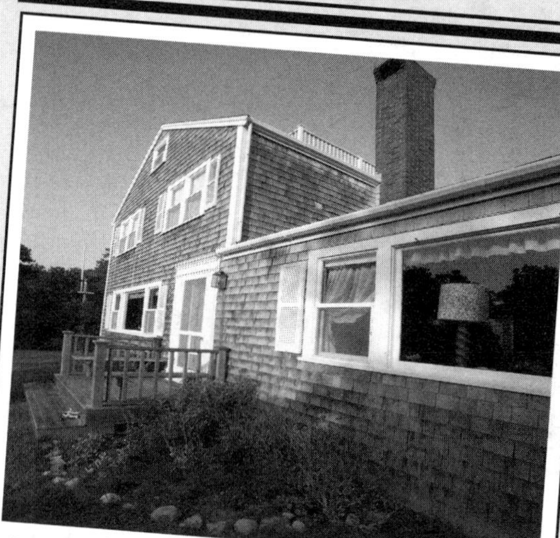

Three-bedroom, two-bath house within walking distance to the beach. Great view. Large open kitchen. All appliances included. Open floor plan. One-car garage. Foundation built on solid rock to be environmentally friendly.

Which House Was Built by a Wise Man and Which by a Foolish Man?

Activity 25 part 2

❊ THIS IS WHAT JESUS HAD TO SAY: ❊

Everyone then who hears these words of mine and acts on them will be like a wise man who built his house on ___________ . (Matthew 7:24)

*And everyone who hears these words of mine and does not act on them will be like a foolish man who built his house on ______.
(Matthew 7:26)*

HINT: See the weather forecast.

WEATHER FORECAST

Hurricane Charley is now off the coast of Cuba and is headed this way. Expected to hit the beach about 6:30 tomorrow morning. It is predicted to be a level-four hurricane.

What to Take?

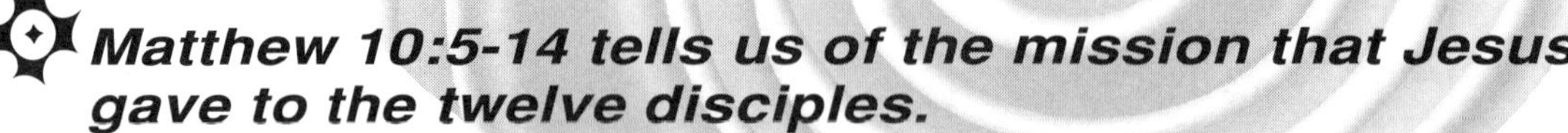

Matthew 10:5-14 tells us of the mission that Jesus gave to the twelve disciples.

Not only does he give them a mission, but he gives very specific directions as to what they should and shouldn't take. Below are the instructions on what not to take (in modern language).

DO NOT TAKE

- money
- suitcase or backpack
- two sets of clothes or extra shoes/sandals
- walking stick (or today that would be a car, bicycle, scooter, roller blades, or other personal vehicle)

Do not make hotel reservations. Rather find someone worthy in the area and stay with them.

That's a lot of things disciples can't take. What do you think they *can* take?

HINT: IT'S TWO WORDS

Feeding Five Thousand

RIDDLE

If you have two loaves of bread and five fish to feed five thousand people for dinner, how many baskets of scraps will you have left over?

PUT THE WORDS BELOW IN THE CORRECT SPACES TO FIGURE OUT WHAT JOHN 6:35 SAYS.

Jesus said to them, "________ am the ________________ of ________________.

________________ comes to ________ will ________________ be ________________,

and ________________ ________________ in ________ will ________________ be ________________."

HINTS:

BREAD comes before ***LIFE***.
HUNGRY comes before ***THIRSTY***.
WHOEVER is immediately before ***comes*** and also immediately after ***and***.

BELIEVES	ME
BREAD	NEVER
HUNGRY	NEVER
I	THIRSTY
LIFE	WHOEVER
ME	WHOEVER

WHO DO YOU SAY THAT I AM?

Jesus asked Peter, "Who do you say that I am?" Peter answered this question. So did some other people with word or actions. Can you follow the clues to match the person with their response?

- *At Jesus' birth they traveled a long way to see him. They said Jesus was "king of the Jews." (Matthew 2:2)*
- *A Roman soldier said, "Truly this man was God's Son!" (Matthew 27:54)*
- *Jesus' faithful disciple was asked to take care of the church. He replied to the question by saying: "You are the Messiah, the Son of the living God." (Matthew 16:16)*
- *He baptized Jesus. People asked him if he was the Messiah. He replied, "I am not the Messiah, but I have been sent ahead of him." (John 3:28)*
- *We often remember her as always being busy, and yet she was one of the first to recognize who Jesus was. She said, "Yes, Lord, I believe that you are the Messiah, the Son of God, the one coming into the world." (John 11:27)*
- *This disciple needed proof Jesus had risen from the dead. When he saw Jesus he said, "My Lord and my God!" (John 20:28)*

▲ CENTURION AT FOOT OF THE CROSS

▲ MARTHA

▲ PETER

▲ THOMAS

▲ JOHN THE BAPTIST

▲ THE WISE MEN

ACTIVITY 29

INSTRUCTIONS

When Jesus was transfigured on the mountain, God said, "This is my Son." Starting with T and ending with N follow the lines from the letters at the TOP to the letters at the BOTTOM. Write down the letters you find—in order—to discover God's instructions to us about Jesus (from Matthew 17:5).

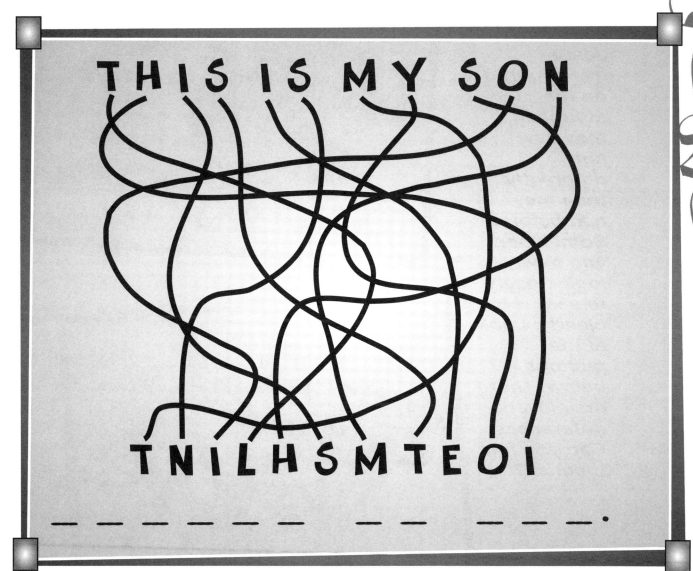

THIS IS MY SON

TNILHSMTEOI

_ _ _ _ _ _ _   _ _   _ _ _.

What's Changed?

When Peter, James, and John saw Jesus transfigured on the mountain, they saw him differently than they had before. Sometimes you have to look closely to see clearly. Look at the pictures below. There are eleven differences. Can you find them all?

NEW TESTAMENT

Mysteries, Riddles, Puzzles AND MORE

PART 2

The Raising of Lazarus Through the Early Church

Patterns and Shapes Graph

Activity 31

When Lazarus died, Jesus wept. Jesus, then, raised Lazarus from the dead. Jesus then said something. Use the code of patterns and shapes below to figure out what Jesus said.

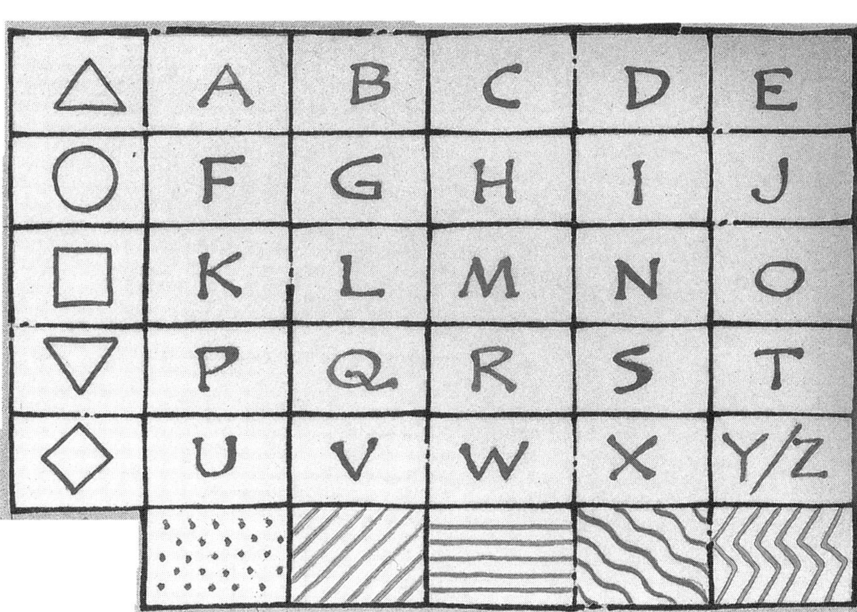

EXAMPLE: A = 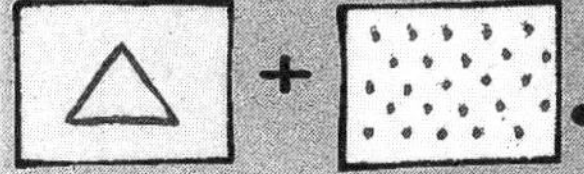

___ ___ ___ ___ ___ ___, ___ ___ ___ ___ ___ ___

___ ___ ___ ___ ___ ___ ___ ___ ___ ___ ___ ___

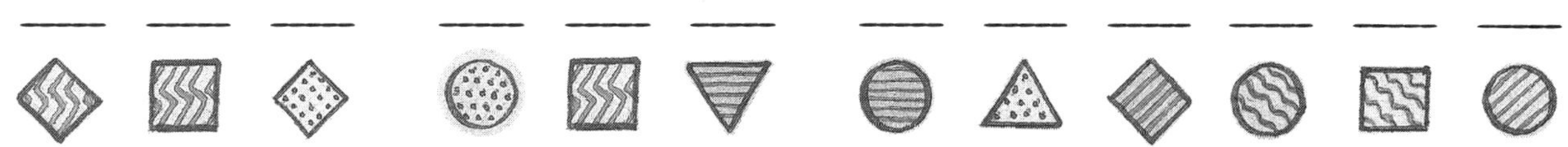

___ ___ ___ ___ ___ ___ ___. (John 11:41b)

ACTIVITY 32

The Case of the Missing Consonants

Someone took out all our consonants and left us only vowels. If you can figure out which consonants to put in, you will discover what the blind man Bartimaeus said to Jesus (Mark 10:47b). (The consonants are listed above the verse. Cross out each consonant as it is used.)

C DD F H J MM NN R SSS VV

___ E ___ U ___ ,

___ O ___

O ___

___ A ___ I ___ ,

___ A ___ E

___ E ___ ___ Y

O ___

___ E.

The Case of Mary and the Expensive Oil

Judas was really upset. One of the women who admired Jesus used very expensive oil to anoint Jesus' feet instead of selling the oil and giving the money to the poor. All we know for sure is that her name was Mary. From the clues, can you figure out which Mary was accused of wastefulness by Judas?

HERE IS THE CASE AGAINST EACH SUSPECT:

▲ **Mary, Mother of Jesus**
She loves her son very much. She is very worried about him. She would spare no expense in honoring him.

▲ **Mary, Mother of John Mark**
She is a woman of wealth. Probably doesn't think the oil is that expensive. It would be easy for her to use what she has on hand.

▲ **Mary Magdalene**
She follows Jesus around and is known to have great admiration for him. Like Mary, mother of Jesus, she would probably spare no expense in honoring Jesus.

▲ **Mary of Bethany**
Sister of Martha and Lazarus. She neglected her duties to sit and learn from Jesus. Jesus raised her brother, Lazarus, from the dead. She is probably very grateful and wishes to honor Jesus.

HERE ARE SOME FACTS:

1 *This incident took place outside of Jerusalem. There is no reason to think that Mary Magdalene was with the disciples at this time.*

2 *There is no indication that the Mary with the oil is related to Jesus.*

3 *Jesus was anointed with oil while in Bethany.*

4 *Mary, mother of John Mark, has an alibi for the time in question. She was busy running her large household.*

NOTE:

Jesus dropped all charges against Mary. He said, "Leave her alone. She bought it so that she might keep it for the day of my burial. You always have the poor with you, but you do not always have me." (John 12:7-8)

?

Would Judas really dare say anything against Jesus' own mother?

PALM SUNDAY

The first day of Holy Week is Palm Sunday (PS). Below cross out all the PS's and you will discover what the people shouted.

H O P S S A P S N N A P S B L E P S S

S E D I P S S T H E O P S N E P S W H O P S

C O P S M E S I P S N T H E P S N A P S

M E P S O P S F T H E P S L O P S R D T H

E P S K I P S N G O P S F I P S S R A E P S L

You might want to check your answer in John 12:13b.

A vowel always appears before PS.

Amazing Foot Trail

Activity 35

Starting with the foot in the top right corner, find the correct trail that tells what Jesus told his disciples after he washed their feet (John 13:15).

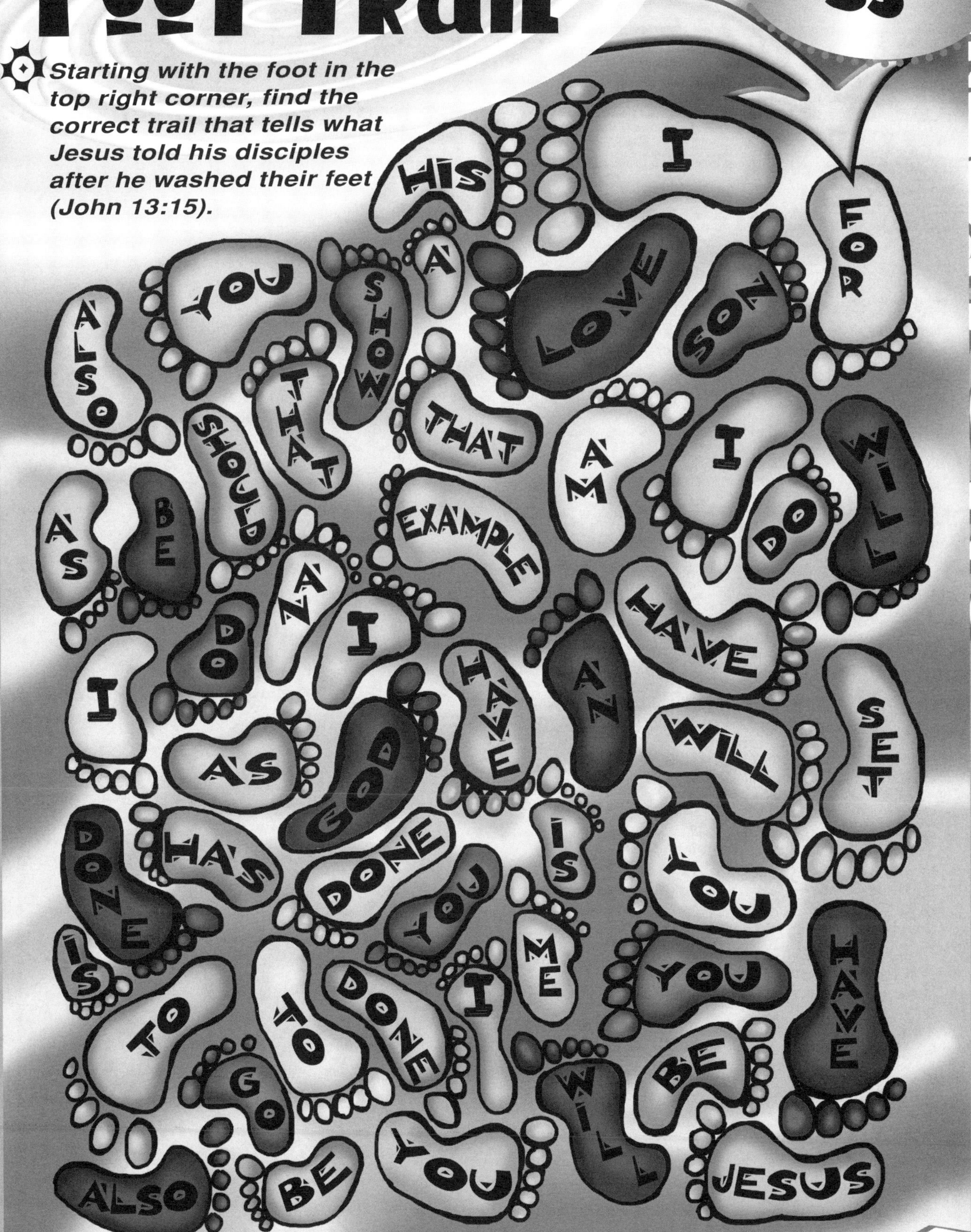

ACTIVITY 36

CONNECT THE DOTS

Connect the dots to discover what's happening.

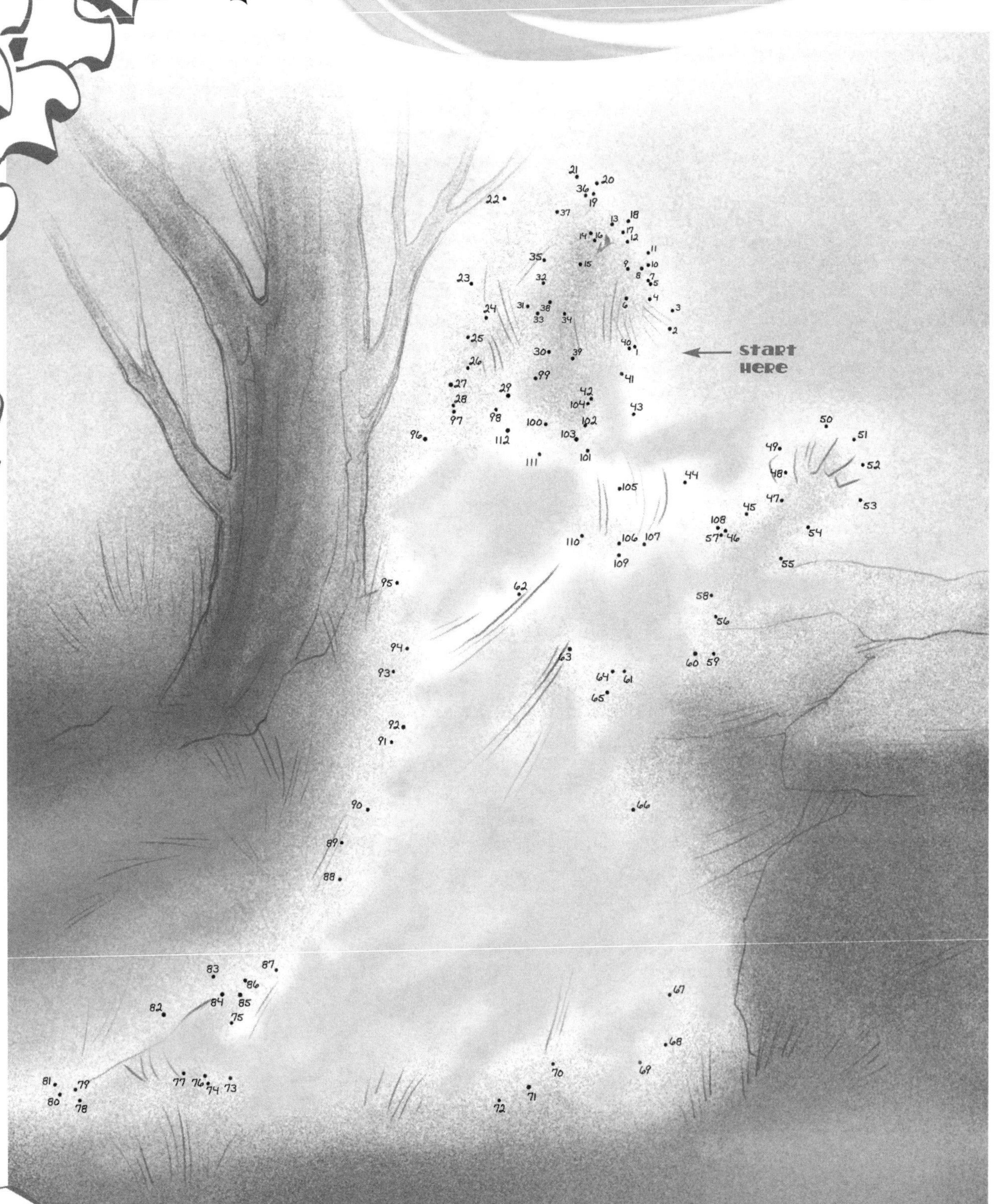

CRUCIFIXION

ACTIVITY 37

Jesus was crucified on the cross. Look at the words below and decide which one in each set is different from the others. Put the first letter of the different word in the box to discover the name of the place where Jesus was crucified.

GARDEN	MUSEUM	HOSPITAL	SCHOOL	
CARROT	SPINACH	ORANGE	CABBAGE	
JEANS	BIRD	LEMON	MOON	
SNEAKERS	GLOVES	BOOTS	SANDALS	
OPEN	CLOSE	SHUT	SEAL	
OCTOBER	JUNE	TUESDAY	DECEMBER	
US	HE	THEY	THEM	
DOG	CAT	HAMSTER	ALLIGATOR	

CAUTION:

The third one is tricky.

How Many?

How many people saw Jesus after the Resurrection and before he ascended into heaven?

Use your Bible to figure out how many people saw him.

✱ AT THE TOMB:

LUKE 24:10

____

✱ BEHIND CLOSED DOORS:

JOHN 20:19, 24

____

✱ ON THE ROAD TO EMMAUS:

LUKE 24:13; 18

____

✱ BEHIND CLOSED DOORS:

JOHN 20:26-29

____

✱ AT ONE TIME:

I CORINTHIANS 15:6

____

Jesus appeared to more than ___ people between his resurrection and his ascension into heaven.

NOTE: In one sighting it says "the other women with them." Another sighting says "more than." Because of this we don't know exactly how many others saw Jesus. That's why the answer line says "more than" before the number.

NOTE: You can't count the same people twice.

What's with the Sheep?

Activity 39

Unscramble the letters on the sheep below to figure out what Jesus told Peter at their last meeting.

We've cheated and added extra letters. Use only the letters found on sheep playing a musical instrument.

CREATE YOUR OWN LANGUAGE

People from around the world were gathered in Jerusalem for Pentecost. When the Holy Spirit descended upon the disciples they spoke to these people in their own languages.

All of them were filled with the Holy Spirit and began to speak in other languages, as the Spirit gave them ability. (Acts 2:4)

Just for fun, use nonsense words to create your own language and then choose a Bible verse to write in that language.

HINTS:

ALL LANGUAGES NEED NOUNS.
ALL LANGUAGES NEED VERBS.
YOU NEED SOME WAY TO DISTINGUISH BETWEEN YOU AND ME.

*

BECAUSE OF TIME, MAKE UP ONLY ENOUGH WORDS IN YOUR OWN LANGUAGE TO WRITE THE CHOSEN BIBLE VERSE.

HINTS:

START WITH A LANGUAGE YOU KNOW AND BUILD ON THAT.

*

MAKING UP A LANGUAGE TOO HARD?
MAKE UP A CODE USING SYMBOLS OR NUMBERS FOR EACH LETTER OF THE ALPHABET

OR

USE ENGLISH AND CHANGE ONE OR TWO LETTERS IN EACH WORD.

You can use all or part of one of these Bible verses:

▲ACTS 1:8 ▲ACTS 2:38 ▲MATTHEW 5:7
▲LUKE 10:27 ▲JOHN 3:16

● WRITE YOUR CODE OR HINTS ABOUT YOUR LANGUAGE HERE:

● WRITE YOUR BIBLE VERSE IN YOUR NEW LANGUAGE HERE:

NOW SEE IF A FRIEND CAN FIGURE OUT THE BIBLE VERSE.

Seven Chosen to Serve

Acts 6 tells us that the early church chose seven men to serve the needs of the widows and orphans.

Below are the names of the seven chosen. Within each name is contained at least one common word. Can you figure out what word or words each name contains? (The number after each name is the number of letters in the word within the name. More than one number means more than one word.) You might come up with something different. We've underlined one word as an example.

- STEPHEN (4, 3)
- PHILIP (3)
- PROCHORUS (6)
- NICANOR (3, 2)
- TIMON (2)
- PARMENAS (3, 2 OR 3, 2)
- NICOLAUS (4, 2)

Questions About Paul

Use the information below to figure out the answer to these questions about Paul.

- WAS PAUL AN APOSTLE OR A DISCIPLE OF JESUS?
- WHEN WAS SAUL'S NAME CHANGED TO PAUL? WHY WAS IT CHANGED?
- WHO SPOKE UP FOR PAUL AND DEFENDED HIM BEFORE THE DISCIPLES?
- WHY WASN'T PAUL TRUSTED AT FIRST BY THE OTHER DISCIPLES?
- HOW MANY MISSIONARY JOURNEYS DID PAUL MAKE?

- *Saul was of the Pharisee class. He approved of the stoning of Stephen. He was on his way to Damascus to arrest Christians when Jesus appeared to him on the road.*
- *Barnabas went with Paul on his first missionary journey. However, they split up. Silas (then Timothy) traveled with Paul the next time he went out. Another journey was made because of a problem in the church at Ephesus.*
- *Saul is a Hebrew name. Paul is a Greek name. The last time we hear him called Saul is in Acts 13 when he and Barnabas are commissioned. We do not know why he is always called Paul after that.*
- *A disciple is someone who is a student and follower of a religious leader. The word apostle means "one sent out." An apostle is a messenger. The apostles in the New Testament carried the message of the good news of Jesus Christ.*

Early Church Word Search

As the early Christian church spread, there were lots of new Christians. Can you find the names of the ten Christians listed below in the word search?

A	Q	U	I	L	A	W	C	E
K	L	B	U	S	L	V	U	A
E	O	L	H	C	P	N	I	E
D	I	E	I	O	I	D	M	K
O	S	U	H	C	Y	T	U	E
R	D	I	E	L	S	O	B	P
C	O	R	N	E	L	I	U	S
A	R	Y	A	D	O	H	R	T
S	H	N	W	E	F	G	I	P

EUNICE and LOIS (Lystra)
DORCAS (Joppa)
CORNELIUS (Caesarea)
RHODA (Jerusalem)
LYDIA (Thyatira)
PRISCILLA and AQUILA (Rome and Corinth)
EUTYCHUS (Troas)
CHLOE (Corinth)

Match the Map

Match each person listed in Activity 43 with his or her place on the map below. (Priscilla and Aquila moved around.)

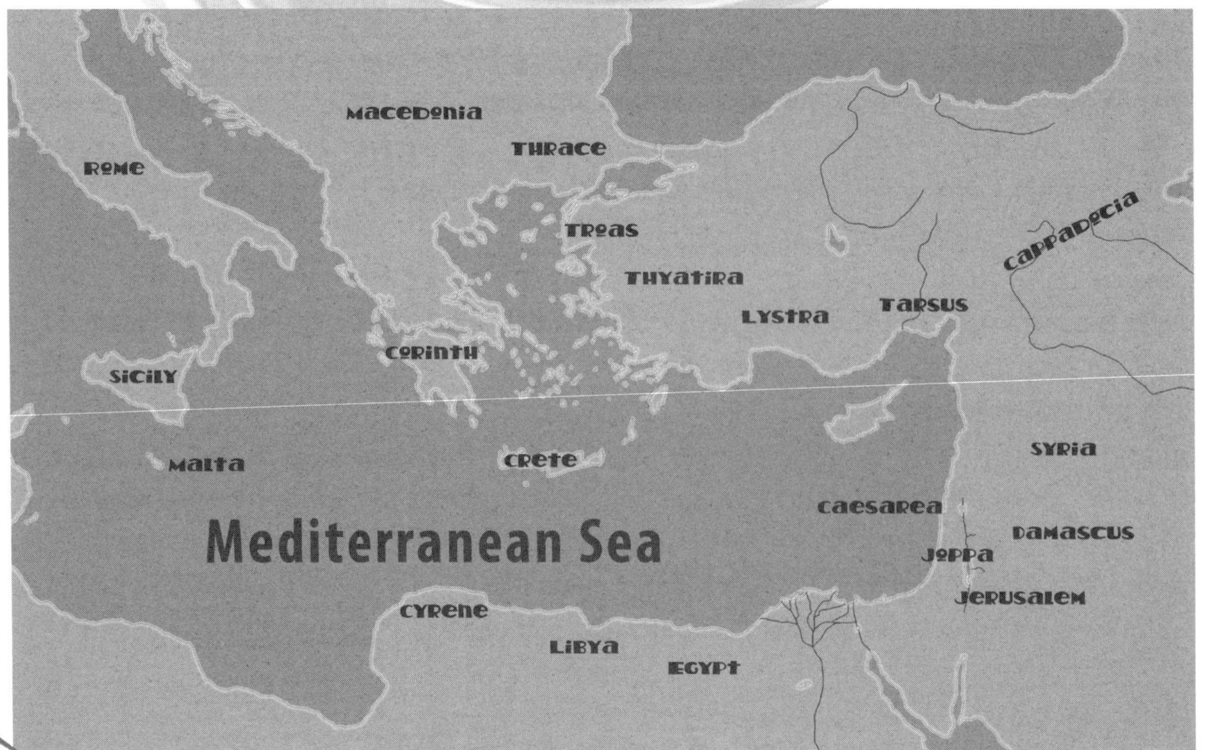

SUMMER BIBLE

Mysteries, Riddles, Puzzles AND MORE

Living God's Word, Discipleship Instructions, Learning God's Word

I NEED HELP!

ACTIVITY 45

Find all the letters that go with each shape. Unscramble them to spell a word. When you have all of the words, you will know what we should ask of God. (See Psalm 25:5a.)

ACTIVITY 46

Paul's Pals

Paul and some of his friends have had their picture taken. One of the people in the picture helped Paul out but has never been a close friend. Can you identify each person in the photo and figure out which person has never been his close friend?

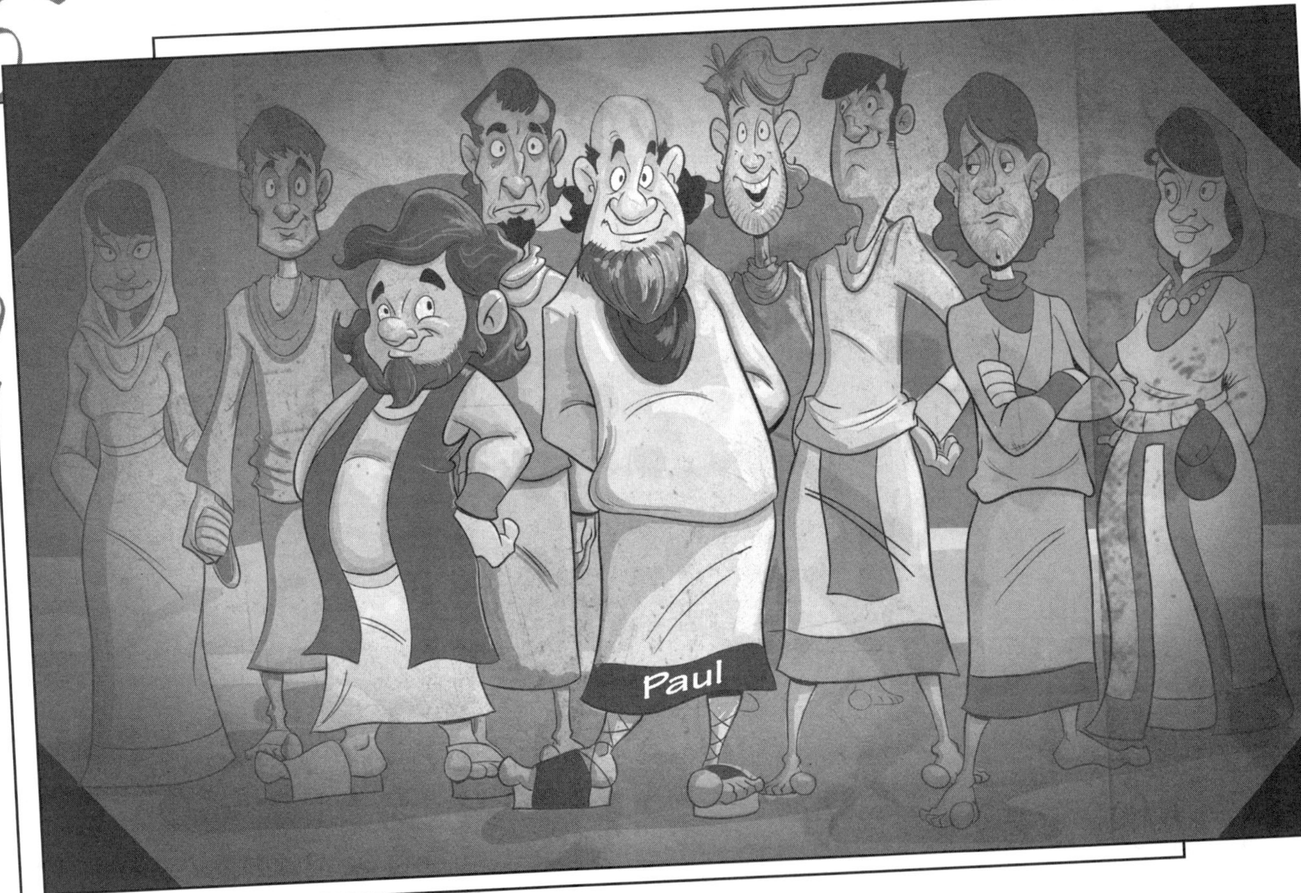

* It is important to remember that even the best of friends sometimes have disagreements and get upset with one another. However, good friends usually patch things up.

* Silas stuck with Paul a long time. He even got thrown into prison with him. It takes a pretty good friend to get in trouble with you (in the name of the Lord) and yet not abandon you. Maybe that's why Silas is standing on Paul's right. (Not your right, Paul's right).

Barnabas' cousin John (also known as John Mark) decided to leave Paul and Barnabas in Perga and return to Jerusalem. Barnabas and Paul had a falling out about this and so Barnabas didn't go with Paul on his second missionary journey.

Dearest Timothy,

Your grandmother and I really miss you since you left on your travels with Paul. We're sending this family picture to keep with you at all times.

ITINERARY

- *Antioch in Syria (take Barnabas and John)*
- *Seleucia and Cyprus*
- *Paphos*
- *Perga in Pamphylia (take Barnabas and ~~John~~)*
- *Antioch in Pisidia*
- *Iconium*
- *Lystra and Derbe*
- *Antioch in Syria*
- *Jerusalem*
- *Derbe and Lystra (take Silas and Timothy)*
- *Troas*
- *Samothrace*
- *Neapolis*
- *Philippi*
- *Thessalonica*
- *Beroea*
- *Athens (Silas and Timothy must stay and work)*
- *Corinth*
- *Antioch*
- *Ephesus*
- *Macedonia*
- *Greece*
- *Troas*
- *Miletus*
- *Jerusalem*

Isn't that cute? Priscilla and Aquila have been married all these years and they still like to hold hands. They are very good friends of Paul.

Timothy was a young Christian man full of power and grace. He was trained in the faith by his mother and his grandmother. Haven't we seen his name somewhere?

Dear Ananias,

I know that you don't trust Paul. However, I am grateful that you followed the Lord's command and baptized him. He is doing a lot of good work spreading the good news of Jesus Christ.

I'm sure you have heard that Paul and I had a falling out when my cousin John Mark left us. However, Paul and I still remain friends; it was just time for us to work separately.

Keep the faith,
Barnabas

Paul,

If you ever come this way and if you have judged me to be faithful to the Lord, please come and stay at my home.

Gratefully,
Lydia

IN THE PICTURE OF PAUL AND HIS BUDDIES, JOHN MARK IS STANDING BETWEEN HIS COUSIN AND LYDIA.

True or False?

ACTIVITY 47

Read each statement below. If the statement is true, write the first letter of the statement in the square on the left. If it is false, write the first letter of the statement in the square on the right. To discover something you should do, read down the left column and then the right column. Check your answer in 1 Timothy 4:12b.

True	Statement	False
	Simon Peter was a disciple of Jesus.	
	Exodus is the second book of the Old Testament.	
	All people in the world are Christians.	
	Titus is the name of a book in the New Testament.	
	There are 66 books in the Bible.	
	Numbers is a book in the New Testament.	
	Hallelujah is a word praising God.	
	Ezekiel was a prophet.	
	Exodus is the book of the Bible that tells about Esther.	
	X-rays were common in Bible times.	
	Amos was one of the twelve disciples.	
	Bread is a symbol of communion.	
	Esther was a queen.	
	Martha was the mother of Jesus.	
	Leviticus is the third book in the Bible.	
	Inviting a lonely friend to church is a good thing to do.	
	Each of the four Gospels is named after a person.	
	Psalms and Proverbs are New Testament books.	
	V is used in the names of only three books of the Bible.	
	Easter celebrates the resurrection of Jesus.	
	Revelation is the last book of the Bible.	
	Lucy is the name of one of the four Gospels.	
	Samuel anointed Saul king of Israel.	
	Esther was the cousin of Moses.	

ACTIVITY 48

They're a PUZZLE

Cut out the pieces of the jigsaw puzzle. When put together correctly, this is the shape the puzzle will be, and you will discover three very important Bible verses. (This is not one of the pieces.)

LEAVE YOUR GIFT THERE BEFORE THE ALTAR AND GO;

THERE IS NO LONGER

BROTHERS AND SISTERS,

THERE IS NO LONGER

MALE AND FEMALE;

FOR ALL OF YOU

ARE ONE IN CHRIST JESUS.

WHEN YOU ARE OFFERING YOUR GIFT AT THE ALTAR,

ACTIVITY 48 part 2

SLAVE OR FREE,

JEW OR GREEK,

AND THEN COME AND OFFER YOUR GIFT. (MATTHEW 5:23-24)

IF YOU REMEMBER THAT YOUR BROTHER OR SISTER HAS SOMETHING AGAINST YOU,

DO NOT BE WEARY

IN DOING WHAT IS RIGHT. (2 THESSALONIANS 3:13)

(GALATIANS 3:28)

FIRST BE RECONCILED TO YOUR BROTHER OR SISTER,

THERE IS NO LONGER

WHAT'S MY NAME?

I am a standard of measure.

I am named after a precious metal.

I'm hard to live up to, but am the standard everyone should measure their lives by.

I'm Matthew 7:12.

WHAT'S MY NAME?

Now unscramble my words below and see if you know more than my name.

NI GHYTEERVNI OD OT SREHOT SA UYO UODWL VEAH MTEH OD OT YUO.

THE GREATEST?

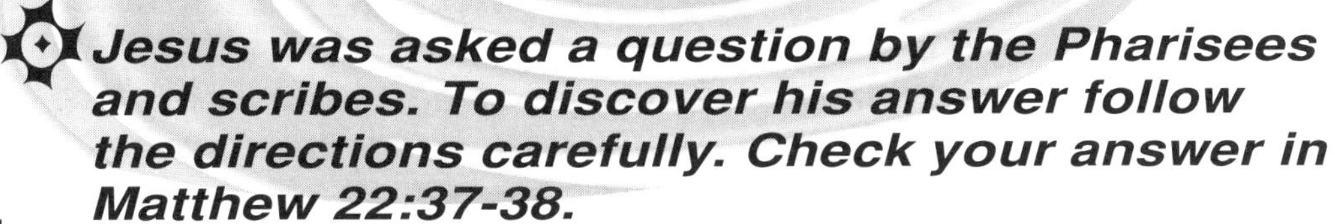

Jesus was asked a question by the Pharisees and scribes. To discover his answer follow the directions carefully. Check your answer in Matthew 22:37-38.

- **Put the letter O in spaces 2, 10, 17, 21, 25, 35, 54, 58, 72, 105.**
- **Put the letter S in spaces 4, 57, 82, 84, 94, 102.**
- **Put the letter H in spaces 5, 14, 30, 38, 49, 67, 80, 86.**
- **Put the letter Y in spaces 1, 20, 34, 53, 71.**
- **Put the letter A in spaces 6, 31, 40, 43, 50, 61, 68, 91, 96, 108.**
- **Put the letter L in spaces 7, 8, 9, 16, 32, 33, 51, 52, 60, 69, 70.**
- **Put the letter E in spaces 12, 15, 39, 87, 90, 93, 112.**
- **Put the letter T in spaces 13, 29, 42, 48, 66, 79, 85, 92, 95, 103, 114.**
- **Put the letter U in spaces 3, 22, 36, 55, 59, 73.**
- **Put the letter R in spaces 18, 23, 37, 41, 56, 74, 89, 101.**
- **Put the letter D in spaces 19, 26, 45, 63, 78, 98, 110**
- **Put the letter G in spaces 24, 88.**
- **Put the letter V in space 11.**
- **Put the letter W in spaces 27, 46, 64.**
- **Put the letter I in spaces 28, 47, 65, 76, 81, 83, 100.**
- **Put the letter N in spaces 44, 62, 77, 97, 109, 113.**
- **Put the letter M in spaces 75, 106, 107, 111.**
- **Put the letter F in space 99.**
- **Put the letter C in space 104.**

__ __ __   __ __ __ __ __   __ __ __ __
1 2 3   4 5 6 7 8   9 10 11 12

__ __ __   __ __ __ __   __ __ __ __   __ __ __
13 14 15   16 17 18 19   20 21 22 23   24 25 26

__ __ __ __   __ __ __   __ __ __ __
27 28 29 30   31 32 33   34 35 36 37

__ __ __ __ __,   __ __ __   __ __ __ __
38 39 40 41 42   43 44 45   46 47 48 49

__ __ __   __ __ __ __   __ __ __ __,
50 51 52   53 54 55 56   57 58 59 60

__ __ __   __ __ __ __   __ __ __   __ __ __ __
61 62 63   64 65 66 67   68 69 70   71 72 73 74

__ __ __ __.   __ __ __ __   __ __   __ __ __
75 76 77 78   79 80 81 82   83 84   85 86 87

__ __ __ __ __ __ __ __   __ __ __   __ __ __ __ __
88 89 90 91 92 93 94 95   96 97 98   99 100 101 102 103

__ __ __ __ __ __ __ __ __ __ __.
104 105 106 107 108 109 110 111 112 113 114

ACTIVITY 51

THE SECOND COMMANDMENT

To discover what commandment Jesus says is second only to the greatest commandment, write the first letter of the name of each item on the line below it. Check your answer by reading Matthew 22:39.

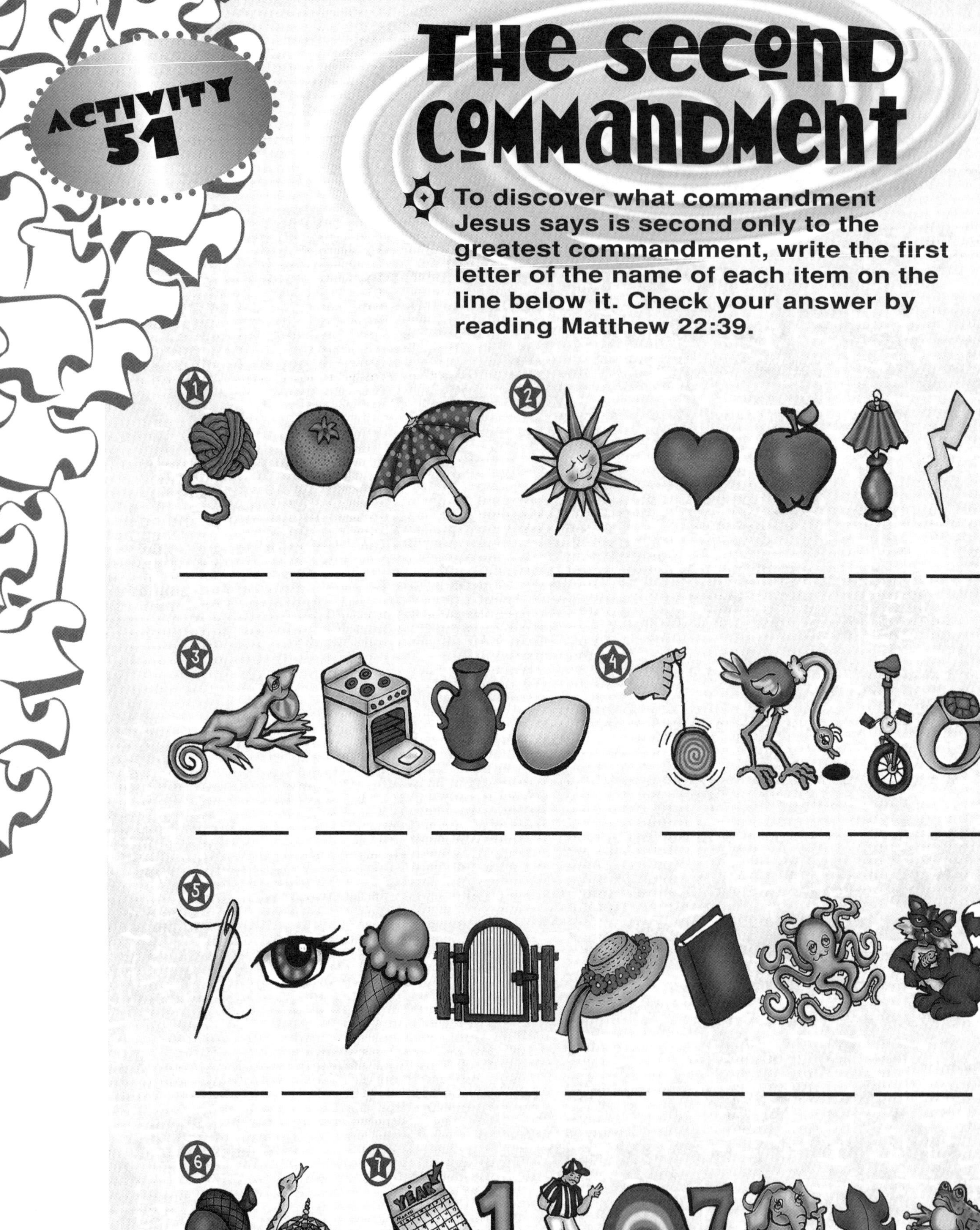

WHAT YOU DO

ACTIVITY 52

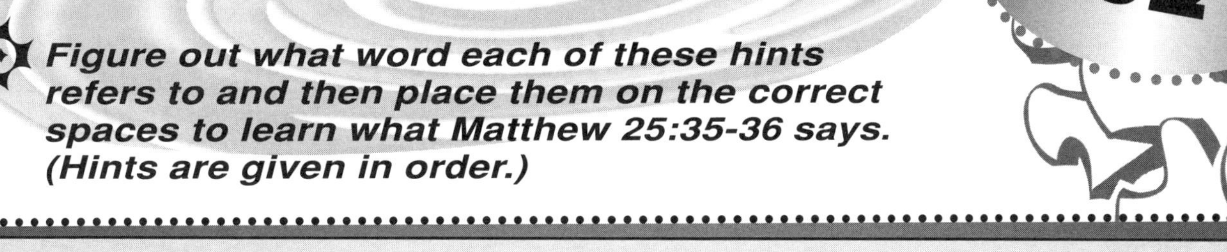

Figure out what word each of these hints refers to and then place them on the correct spaces to learn what Matthew 25:35-36 says. (Hints are given in order.)

1. When you go without anything to eat for a long time and your stomach begins to growl, you are what?

2. What you need if you're suffering from hint number 1.

3. If you wander around in a desert for a long time without water, you become what?

4. After you eat something really salty you want something to ____________ .

5. Someone you meet for the first time is a ____________ .

6. To be hospitable. To make someone feel good when they come to visit you. (past tense)

7. What you are when you get into a bathtub (besides wet).

8. When you get dressed, what do you put on ? (Use the "ing" form of the word.)

9. When you don't feel well you are ____________.

10. When you were a baby someone ____________ ____________ ______ you. (3 words)

11. If you have committed a serious crime, you will be sent here.

12. When you went to see someone at their home, you ____________ them.

FOR I WAS ____________ AND YOU GAVE ME ____________, I WAS ____________ AND YOU GAVE ME SOMETHING TO ____________, I WAS A ____________ AND YOU ____________ ME, I WAS ____________ AND YOU GAVE ME ____________, I WAS ____________ AND YOU ____________ ____________ ____________ ME, I WAS IN ____________ AND YOU ____________ ME.

Repeats

In the Bible verse below we have left out all the words that are repeated. How quickly can you figure out what Matthew 25:40 says? We have given you some hints to help you out.

Truly I tell ______ , just as ______ ______ ______ ______ one
(3) (3) (2) (1) (5)

______ the least ______ these who are members ______ my family,
(4) (4) (4)

______ ______ ______ ______ me.
(3) (2) (1) (5)

HINTS:

1. NOT *HE*, NOT *SHE*, BUT ______ . TWO-LETTER WORD.
2. PAST TENSE OF THE VERB *DO*.
3. THREE-LETTER PRONOUN. NOT *ME*, BUT ______ .
4. TWO-LETTER PREPOSITION. EXAMPLE: BELONGS BETWEEN SON ______ GOD.
5. TWO-LETTER WORD. ENDS IN *O*.

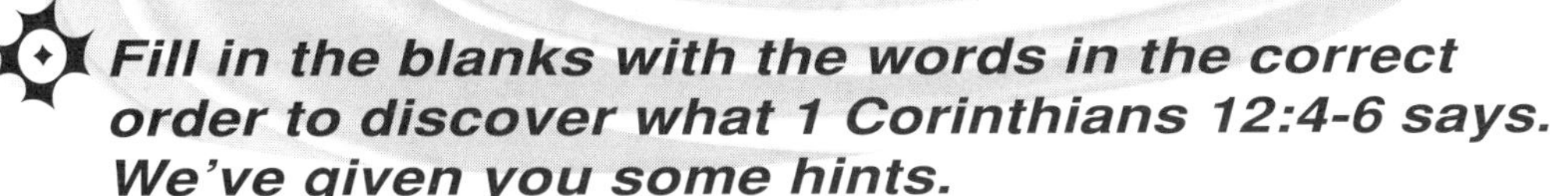

NUMBER OF Letters

ACTIVITY 54

Fill in the blanks with the words in the correct order to discover what 1 Corinthians 12:4-6 says. We've given you some hints.

2 letters		4 letters	6 letters	9 letters
IN	ARE	LORD	SPIRIT	VARIETIES
IS	ARE	SAME		VARIETIES
IT	ARE	SAME		VARIETIES
OF	BUT	SAME		
OF	BUT	THEM		
OF	BUT			
OF	GOD			
	NOW	**5 letters**	**8 letters**	**10 letters**
	THE	GIFTS	EVERYONE	ACTIVATES
3 letters	THE	THERE	SERVICES	ACTIVITIES
ALL	THE	THERE		
AND	WHO	THERE		

N__ _____ _R_ _________ __ ____S,

B__ ___ ____ _____; _N_ _____ ___

_________ _F S______S, ___ T__ ____

L___; _N_ _____ ___ _________ __

_________, _U_ __ _S ___ ____ __D

W__ A________ __L __ T___ _N

________.

Take the Challenge!

Below are two boxes. One is full of troubles that result from relying on our wants and desires. The other contains things that come to us because of a good relationship with God.

Can you figure out what the title of each box is?

Then see if you can figure out where to put all the words in the clueless crossword.

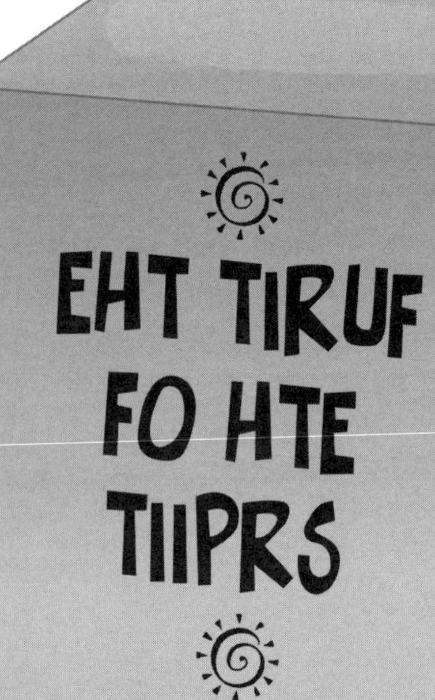

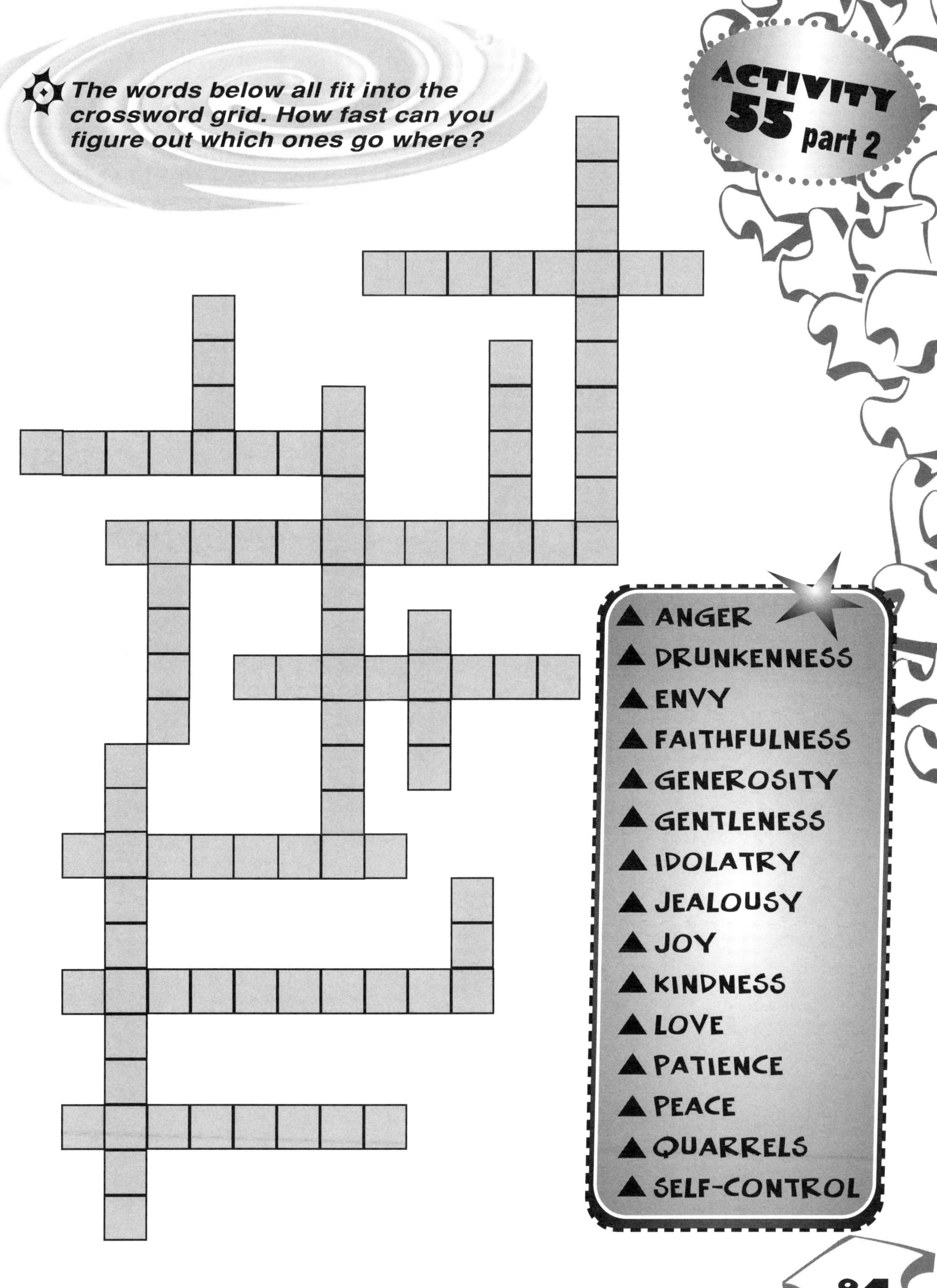
ACTIVITY
55 part 2
The words below all fit into the crossword grid. How fast can you figure out which ones go where?
ANGER
DRUNKENNESS
ENVY
FAITHFULNESS
GENEROSITY
GENTLENESS
IDOLATRY
JEALOUSY
JOY
KINDNESS
LOVE
PATIENCE
PEACE
QUARRELS
SELF-CONTROL

ACTIVITY
55 part 3
IF YOU HAVE TROUBLE, READ
GALATIANS 5:19-23.

Okay, now, which words go in which box?

Label the boxes with the names you unscrambled on page 80. Then take the words from the clueless crossword and write each somewhere on the box you think it goes in.

GOD can Handle It

ACTIVITY 56

Life can be wonderful and fun or life can really be hard to handle. Whatever you're feeling, take it to God. God can handle it!

Here are a few feelings expressed in the Book of Psalms. What emotion do you think the writer was expressing in each of these statements?

NOTE: Don't worry about our answers or anybody else's. What do you think?

- O LORD, do not rebuke me in your anger, or discipline me in your wrath. (Psalm 38:1)
- I say to God, my rock, "Why have you forgotten me? Why must I walk about mournfully because the enemy oppresses me?" (Psalm 42:9)
- Vindicate me, O God, and defend my cause. (Psalm 43:1a)
- O come, let us sing to the LORD; let us make a joyful noise to the rock of our salvation! (Psalm 95:1)
- I lie awake; I am like a lonely bird on the housetop. (Psalm 102:7)
- I love the LORD, because he has heard my voice and my supplications. (Psalm 116:1)
- I wait for the LORD, my soul waits, and in his word I hope. (Psalm 130:5)
- How very good and pleasant it is when kindred live together in unity! (Psalm 133:1)
- Where can I go from your spirit? Or where can I flee from your presence? (Psalm 139:7)
- Deliver me, O LORD, from evildoers; protect me from those who are violent. (Psalm 140:1)

ACTIVITY 57

WRITE YOUR OWN PROVERBS

According to the Contemporary English Version (CEV) of the Bible, Proverbs 1:2 says, "Proverbs will teach you wisdom and self-control and how to understand sayings with deep meanings."

HERE ARE THREE EXAMPLES OF PROVERBS (ALL FROM THE CEV):

1. *Don't tell your neighbor to come back tomorrow, if you can help today. (Proverbs 3:28)*
2. *Fools enjoy doing wrong, but anyone with good sense enjoys acting wisely. (Proverbs 10:23)*
3. *No matter how much you want, laziness won't help a bit, but hard work will reward you. (Proverbs 13:4a)*

NOW IT'S YOUR TURN! WRITE THREE PROVERBS THAT GIVE GOOD ADVICE FOR LIVING FAITHFULLY.

The Case of the Mixed-Up Letters

Activity 58

Manuscripts for the New Testament letters have been found.

Caroline the librarian has been asked to figure out whether they were written to individual people, churches, or another group. She has been asked also to write down the name of who wrote each letter. Then she has to put them in biblical order, and she is not allowed to use the Bible! Can you follow the clues and come to the same conclusion that Caroline did?

- There are twenty-one New Testament letters.
- Paul, James, Peter, John, and Jude all wrote letters.
- If the name of a New Testament letter ends in NS you can count on it being written to a church in some part of the world and that Paul wrote it.
- Timothy and Titus were Paul's friends. Paul wrote letters to friends and to people with problems.
- Romans is the first New Testament letter. Jude, the last letter, comes just before the Book of Revelation.
- The letters to Corinth come right after Romans and immediately before Galatians in the New Testament.
- Revelation is the last book of the New Testament. It is not a letter.

Peter wrote to Christians who needed help in strengthening their faith.

Nobody knows who wrote Hebrews, and we don't know to whom it was written.

NEW TESTAMENT LETTERS FOUND:	CORRECT ORDER (NUMBER THEM):	WRITTEN TO:
COLOSSIANS		
1 CORINTHIANS		
2 CORINTHIANS		
EPHESIANS		
GALATIANS		
HEBREWS		
JAMES		
1 JOHN		
2 JOHN		
3 JOHN		
JUDE		
1 PETER		
2 PETER		
PHILEMON		
PHILIPPIANS		
ROMANS		
1 THESSALONIANS		
2 THESSALONIANS		
1 TIMOTHY		
2 TIMOTHY		
TITUS		

- Letters 6 and 7 are Philippians and Colossians, and they are followed by 1 Thessalonians (all written to churches).
- 1 Timothy is number 10.
- Paul's letters to churches come first in the list of New Testament letters, and his letters to people come right before Hebrews.
- Hebrews comes right before James, the first of the letters not written by Paul.

We don't know who the book of Jude was written to. 1, 2, and 3 John were probably written to churches, but we don't know their names.

- E may come before F in the alphabet, but Galatians comes right before Ephesians in the Bible.
- James, Peter, John, and Jude wrote their letters in this order.
- James wrote to the twelve tribes of the Dispersion (Jews scattered around the world).

NEW TESTAMENT LETTERS FOUND:	CORRECT ORDER (WRITE THEM IN ORDER):	WRITTEN BY:
COLOSSIANS		
1 CORINTHIANS		
2 CORINTHIANS		
EPHESIANS		
GALATIANS		
HEBREWS		
JAMES		
1 JOHN		
2 JOHN		
3 JOHN		
JUDE		
1 PETER		
2 PETER		
PHILEMON		
PHILIPPIANS		
ROMANS		
1 THESSALONIANS		
2 THESSALONIANS		
1 TIMOTHY		
2 TIMOTHY		
TITUS		

- PHILEMON IS A MAN WHOSE SLAVE RAN AWAY TO STAY WITH PAUL.
- TITUS COMES JUST AFTER 2 TIMOTHY AND RIGHT BEFORE PHILEMON.
- PETER'S LETTERS WERE WRITTEN TO ENCOURAGE CHRISTIANS, BUT WE DON' KNOW THEIR NAMES.
- IF YOU HAVEN'T FIGURED IT OUT BY NOW, CHECK YOUR BIBLE.

In Common

❋ What do these three shapes have in common? ❋

❋ What do these things have in common? ❋

SOLUTIONS, ANSWERS, AND POSSIBILITIES

FOR Mysteries, Riddles, Puzzles AND MORE

Activity 1 (p. 7)

In order:

octopus
aardvark
tarantula
kangaroo
walrus
flamingo

Activity 2 (p. 8)

Answers will vary. These are just the names we came up with (except for *pangolin,* which is an actual animal).

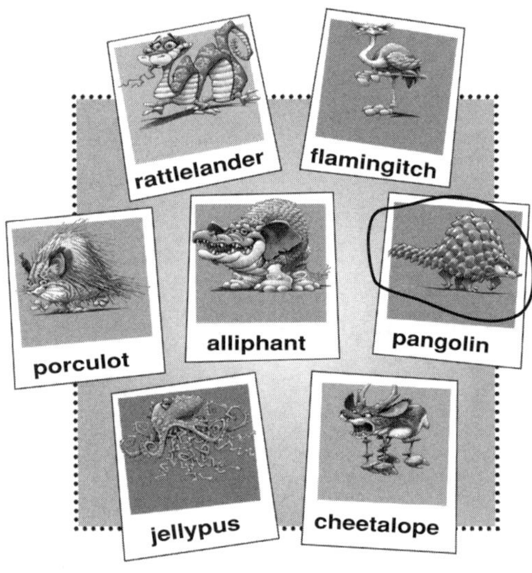

Activity 3 (p. 9)

Genesis 7:2-3—Take with you seven pairs of all clean animals . . . and a pair of the animals that are not clean, . . . and seven pairs of the birds of the air.

The ark was about 450 feet long, 75 feet wide, and 45 feet high.

There were no fish or other aquatic animals on the ark. They didn't need to be, as they could swim and live in the water.

Activity 4 (p. 10)

- Adam—930 years old (Genesis 5:5)
- Seth—912 years old (Genesis 5:8)
- Enosh—905 years old (Genesis 5:11)
- Kenan—910 years old (Genesis 5:14)
- Mahalalel—895 years old (Genesis 5:17)
- Jared—962 years old (Genesis 5:20)
- Enoch—365 years old (Genesis 5:23)
- Methuselah—969 years old (Genesis 5:27)
- Lamech—777 years old (Genesis 5:31)
- Noah—950 years old (Genesis 9:29)

Abraham was 100 years old when Isaac was born. Sarah was either 91 or close to her 91st birthday when Isaac was born! (We don't know what month anybody was born in.)

Activity 5 (p. 11)

Esau was Jacob's twin.

Jacob's name means "heel grabber." (He was born second. He got this name because at birth he "grabbed Esau's foot.") (Genesis 25:24-26)

Jacob's name was changed to *Israel* by God.
(Genesis 32:27-28)

Jacob got Esau to trade his inheritance for a bowl of soup.
(Genesis 25:29-35)

Laban tricked Jacob into marrying his daughter Leah when Jacob thought he was marrying Rachel. (Genesis 29:18-25)

Jacob tricked Laban into giving him the best of his sheep.
(Genesis 30:25-43)

Activity 6 (pp. 12-13)

Joseph's Dreams:
Joseph had a mother, a father, and eleven brothers. Joseph dreamed eleven sheaves and eleven stars, the sun, and the moon bowed down to him. The sheaves and the stars represent Joseph's brothers. The sun and the moon represent his parents. (In astronomy the sun and moon are greater than the stars.) Since we bow to people who are in a position of greater authority than we are and in dreams bowing means the person being bowed to is destined for greatness, Joseph's dreams are telling him that someday he will be greater than his parents and brothers. Someday his family will bow to him. Of course, as a youth Joseph loved to brag to his brothers, so he told them about these dreams. (Genesis 37:5-11)

Dreams Joseph Interpreted:
Joseph told Pharaoh's chief baker that his dream of birds eating bread meant that in three days he would be executed. The baker was executed three days later.

Joseph told Pharaoh's chief cupbearer that his dream about a cup meant that in three days he would begin serving Pharaoh again.
(Genesis 40:7-23)

Pharaoh dreamed of seven good ears of grain and seven bad ones. He dreamed of seven fat cows and seven thin cows. Joseph interpreted this as meaning there would be seven years of plentiful crops and seven years of famine.
(Genesis 41:1-36)

Activity 7 (p. 14)

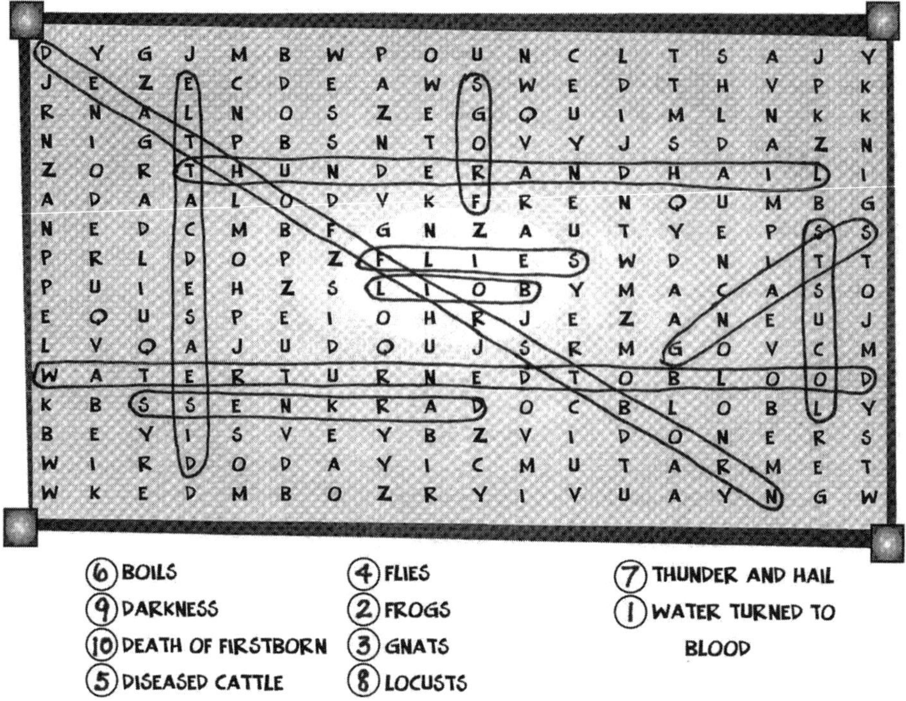

Activity 8 (p. 15)

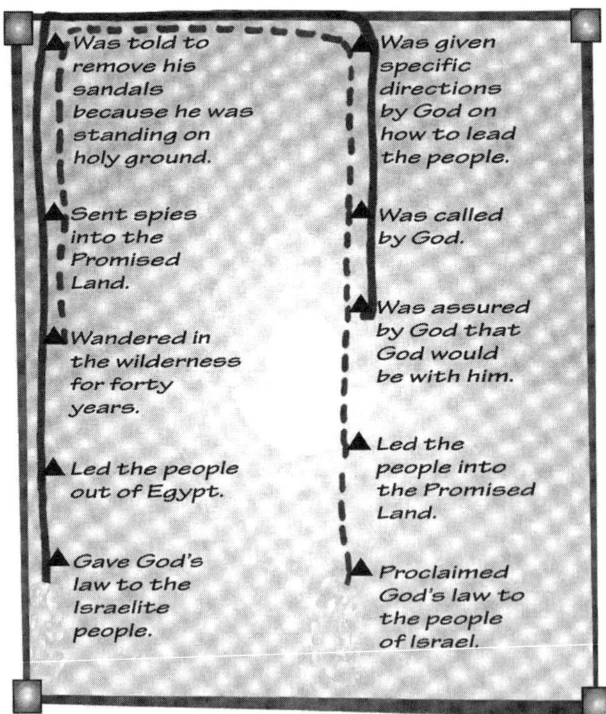

Start on the outside for Moses (solid line) and the inside for Joshua (dotted line) or vice versa.

Only differences: Moses led the people out of Egypt, Joshua led the people into the Promised Land, Moses gave God's law to the Israelites, and Joshua proclaimed God's law to the Israelites.

Activity 9 (pp. 16-19)

1. The guard said Sarah was too old to have a baby. The only reason he would have to say that is that Sarah's portrait must be the one of the elderly woman holding a baby. That makes Sarah's portrait #7. That rules out Abraham as a suspect as he would have no reason to take another portrait.

2. The receptionist said that Rebekah hung out at the local well drawing water for camels. Isn't that a water jar on the head of the woman in portrait #1? That would make Rebekah's portrait #1. That rules out Isaac as a suspect.

3. The gallery director said that Queen Esther wore a lot of jewelry. There's only one portrait in the gallery with a lot of jewelry. That makes portrait #4 a portrait of Esther. As much as we hate to say it, that rules out Haman as a suspect. He wouldn't be bothered with stealing any other portrait.

4. The gallery director said that Ruth was known for baking bread. The woman in portrait #5 must be Ruth. That rules out Boaz as a suspect.

5. The gallery visitor stated that the name Chloe means "blonde." The woman in portrait #3 is blonde. That means #3 must be Chloe. None of the suspects has any connection to Chloe.

6. It was discovered that Eve had a record for pilfering fruit. The only fruit in any portrait is that in portrait #2. That would make portrait #2 Eve's portrait. That rules out Adam as a suspect.

7. The only woman left without a portrait is Deborah the judge, so hers is the missing one. That means Barak must be the thief. He is the only one with a motive for taking the portrait.

Activity 10 (p. 20)

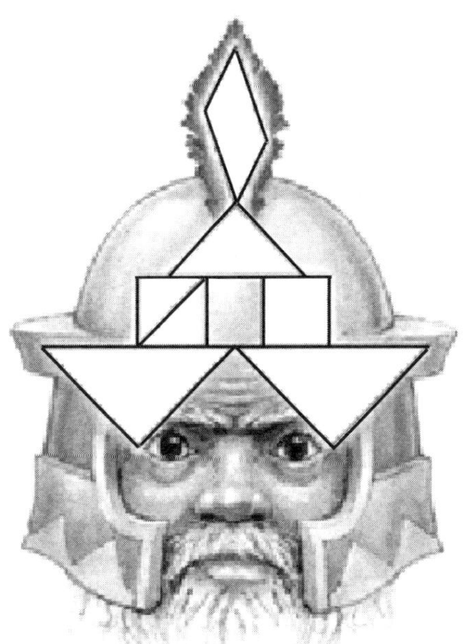

Activity 11 (p. 20)

Trust in the LORD with all your heart,
and do not rely on your own insight.
Proverbs 3:5

Activity 12 (pp. 21-23)

Building Plans:
- acacia wood
- cubits
- gold, inside, outside
- 4, 4
- acacia wood, gold
- mercy seat, gold

The Philistines took the ark the first time.

Joshua made sure the ark was brought into the Promised Land.

David had the ark brought into Jerusalem.

Solomon placed the ark in the Temple.

What's really in the ark?
- the Ten Commandments
- Aaron's rod
- manna

We don't know where the ark is now. There are people who say they can prove each of the three theories.

Activity 13 (p. 24)

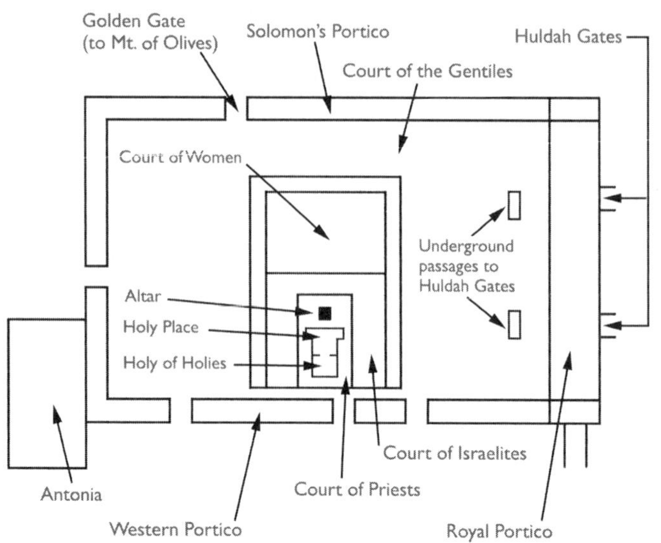

You cannot get into the Holy of Holies. Only the high priest was allowed to enter there.

Activity 14 (p. 25)

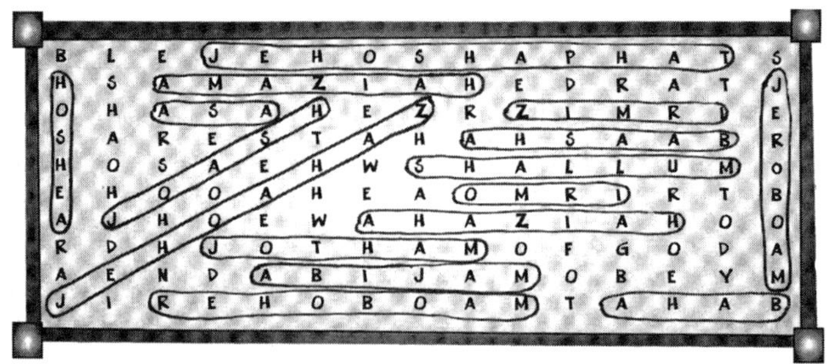

BLES
SEDRAT
HER
ARETH
OSEW
HOHEART
HEWO
RDOFGOD
ANDOBEY
IT

Blessed rather are those who hear the word of God and obey it. (Luke 11:28)

Activity 15 (p. 26)

ACTIVITY 15

Mortal Enemies

Isaiah tells us that when the Messiah comes, peace will reign on the earth. One sign of this is that animals that are normally mortal enemies will learn to live together in peace. Follow the clues to match the animals in Isaiah 11:6-8.

1 One fairy tale says this animal dressed up like Little Red Riding Hood's grandmother. One of its favorite meals is lamb chops.

2 In the nursery rhyme Mary had one of these (it was little), and it followed her to school. To the question, "Who's afraid of the big bad wolf?" this animal would reply, "I am."

3 It is said that this animal will eat anything, including tin cans. Some of them have beards. Baby ones are called "kids."

4 This animal is known for running real fast. People also say it "can't change its spots." It can outrun little tin-can eaters.

5 This animal is really a baby cow or a baby bull. In the peaceable kingdom it gets along with two other animals.

6 This animal likes to roar, especially at baby animals. But in the peaceable kingdom it will get along with two other animals.

7 Of these two animals, one likes to sleep all winter and the other chews its cud. In the peaceable kingdom they will graze together.

8 This animal is very strong and is often used to pull large heavy loads.

9 This animal was roaring earlier and has already been matched with two other animals, but in the peaceable kingdom, this king of the jungle will also eat straw with the strong puller of heavy loads.

10 Mothers usually don't like it when children play with these creatures that slither.

NOTE: A fatling is a cow, goat, or other animal that has grown.

IF YOU WANT TO KNOW WHO'S GOING TO LEAD THEM ALL, READ ISAIAH 11:6.

Can you think of another set of animals that would be mortal enemies? Think up clues to identify them.

Note: The "fatling" could either be the cow or the goat. "Fatling" means an animal that has grown and fattened up. It doesn't matter which lion you matched with the ox or with the two other animals. (One is a female lion and one is male, but that was just to make it tricky.)

Activity 16 (p. 29)

ACTIVITY 16

The Reason for the Season

Advent and Christmas are a time to celebrate the birth of the Messiah, Jesus the Christ. Among all the decorations for the season can you find the Christian symbols?

Activity 17 (pp. 30-32)

Explanation:

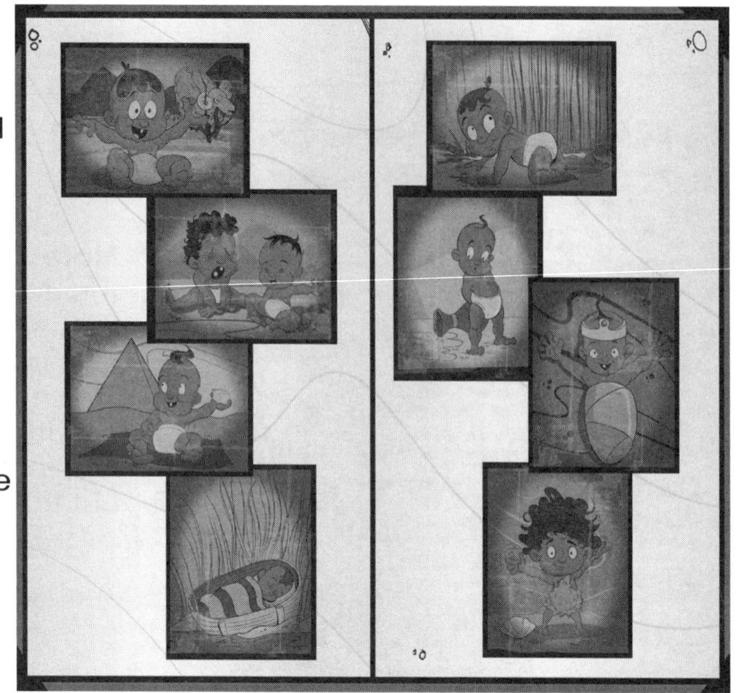

1. Each picture has a visual clue as to the baby's identity.

2. The explanations from the Bible (page 32) are in correct biblical order.

3. Since there were no pictures of Abraham in existence (page 30) and the family tree shows Isaac as Abraham's son, Isaac's picture is first in the new album. His clue is the ram because a ram took his place as a burnt offering.

4. The family tree shows that Jacob is descended from Isaac, and we know that Isaac had a twin brother, Esau (page 30), so Jacob and Esau come next. There is only one picture with two babies, so it must be of the twins, Esau and Jacob.

5. Joseph is next in the album, as he is Jacob's son. Joseph was an important man in Egypt, so the picture with a pyramid is his.

6. Joseph brought the Israelites to Egypt, and Moses led them out, so Moses' picture would be after Joseph's. Moses was hidden in the reeds when he was an infant.

7. Obed was David's grandfather, so he has to come before David, which means he would be next. Since Obed was Ruth's son and she gleaned grain from the field, Obed's picture shows grain.

8. Samuel comes next because he anointed David as king. His picture shows a bottle of oil. There is no picture of David (page 30) so the baby with the crown must be King Solomon, David's son.

9. The only New Testament baby is John the Baptist. Check out the baptism certificate and you will discover the shell symbol. That is the symbol for John the Baptist. He is the last baby in our album.

Activity 18 (pp. 33-35)

In order: Zechariah, Joseph of Nazareth, King Herod, wise man, innkeeper, shepherd

Activity 19 (p. 36)

Matthew 6:11—bread
Exodus 27:20—olives
Psalm 132:17—lamp
Luke 9:3—tunic
Luke 2:7—bands of cloth
(also known as swaddling clothes)

Activity 20 (p. 37)

Water, a shell with three drops, and a descending dove are all symbols of baptism.

Activity 21 (p. 37)

I myself have seen and have testified that this is the Son of God. (John 1:34)

Activity 22 (p. 38)

The Spirit of the Lord is upon me, because he has anointed me to bring good news to the poor. (Luke 4:18)

Activity 23 (pp. 39-40)

James	James / Alphaeus
Andrew	Judas Iscariot
Bartholomew	Judas / James
John	Simon / Zealot
Peter	Philip
Matthew	
Thomas	me / God

Activity 24 (p. 41)

Blessed are the poor in spirit, for theirs is the kingdom of heaven.

Blessed are those who mourn, for they will be comforted.

Blessed are the meek, for they will inherit the earth.

Blessed are those who hunger and thirst for righteousness, for they will be filled.

Blessed are the merciful, for they will receive mercy.

Blessed are the pure in heart, for they will see God.

Blessed are the peacemakers, for they will be called children of God.

Blessed are those who are persecuted for righteousness' sake, for theirs is the kingdom of heaven.

Blessed are you when people revile you and persecute you and utter all kinds of evil against you on my account. Rejoice and be glad, for your reward is great in heaven. (Matthew 5:3-12a)

Activity 25 (pp. 42-43)

Everyone then who hears these words of mine and acts on them will be like a **wise** man who built his house on **rock**. (Matthew 7:24)

And everyone who hears these words of mine and does not act on them will be like a **foolish** man who built his house on **sand**. (Matthew 7:26)

I'd buy the house with a rock foundation.

Activity 26 (p. 44)

good news

Activity 27 (p. 45)

Answer to riddle: *You* wouldn't have any leftovers at all! *You* can't feed five thousand people with two loaves of bread and five fish. That takes a miracle! When Jesus performed this miracle there were twelve baskets of leftovers.

Jesus said to them, "**I** am the **bread** of **life. Whoever** comes to **me** will **never** be **hungry**, and **whoever believes** in **me** will **never** be **thirsty**." (John 6:35)

Activity 28 (p. 46)

- *At Jesus' birth they traveled a long way to see him. They said Jesus was "king of the Jews." (Matthew 2:2)* **THE WISE MEN**
- *Jesus' faithful disciple was asked to take care of the church. He replied to the question by saying: "You are the Messiah, the Son of the living God." (Matthew 16:16)* **PETER**
- *We often remember her as always being busy, and yet she was one of the first to recognize who Jesus was. She said, "Yes, Lord, I believe that you are the Messiah, the Son of God, the one coming into the world." (John 11:27)* **MARTHA**
- *A Roman soldier said, "Truly this man was God's Son!" (Matthew 27:54)* **CENTURION AT THE CROSS**
- *He baptized Jesus. People asked him if he was the Messiah. He replied, "I am not the Messiah, but I have been sent ahead of him." (John 3:28)* **JOHN THE BAPTIST**
- *This disciple needed proof Jesus had risen from the dead. When he saw Jesus he said, "My Lord and my God!" (John 20:28)* **THOMAS**

Activity 29 (p. 47)

LISTEN TO HIM.

Activity 30 (p. 48)

The second photo differs in these ways:

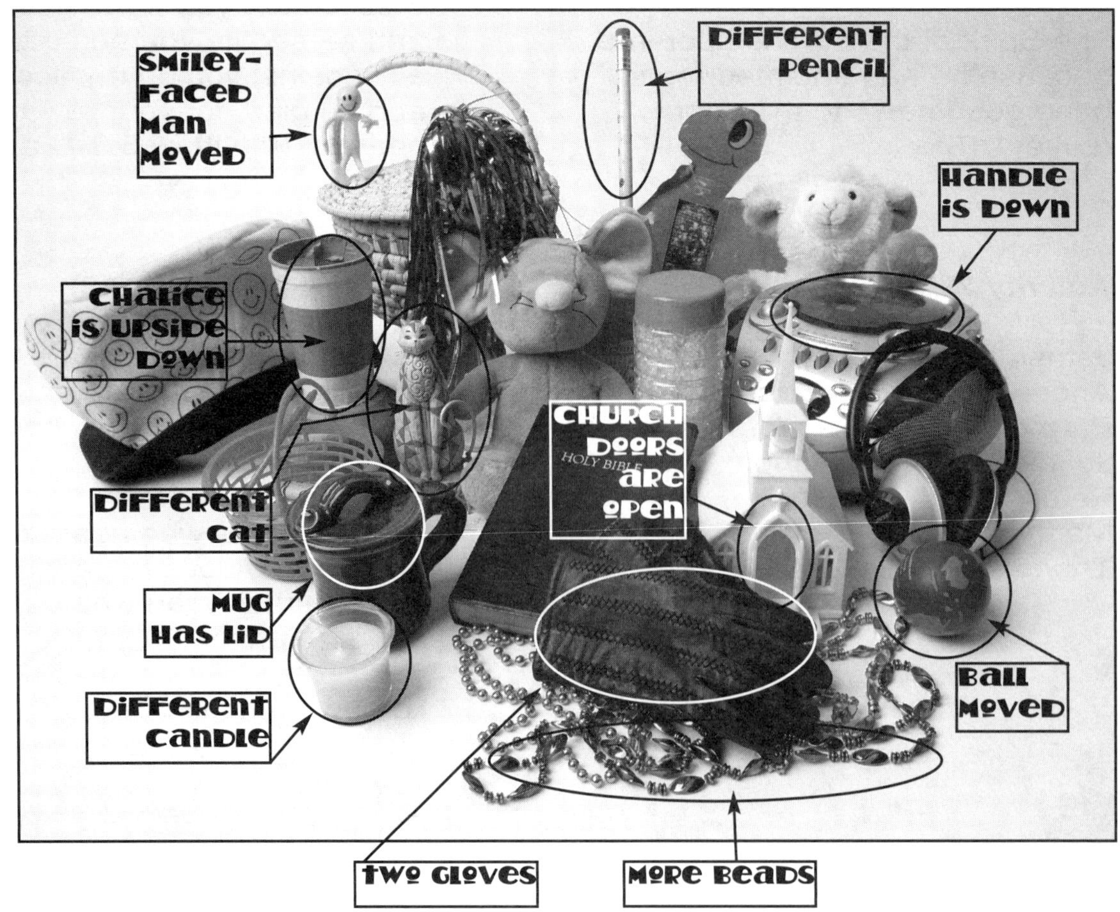

Activity 31 (p. 51)

Father, I thank you for having heard me. (John 11:41b)

Activity 32 (p. 52)

Jesus, son of David, have mercy on me! (Mark 10:47b)

Activity 33 (p. 53)

All of the Marys would have a reason for wanting to honor Jesus by anointing his feet with oil.

Fact 3 states that the anointing took place in Bethany. While we know that Mary Magdalene was at the Crucifixion and Resurrection, there is nothing to say she was in Bethany (Fact 1). Therefore Mary Magdalene was not involved.

The woman with the oil is probably not related to Jesus (Fact 2), and Judas would not dare accuse Jesus' mother of doing anything that could be criticized, so it was not Jesus' mother.

Fact 4 states that it could not have been John Mark's mother.

Therefore, since the anointing took place in Bethany (Fact 3) and all other Marys have been eliminated as suspects, Mary of Bethany must have been the one to anoint Jesus' feet.

Activity 34 (p. 54)

Hosanna! Blessed is the one who comes in the name of the Lord—the King of Israel. (John 12:13b)

Activity 35 (p. 55)

Activity 36 (p. 56)

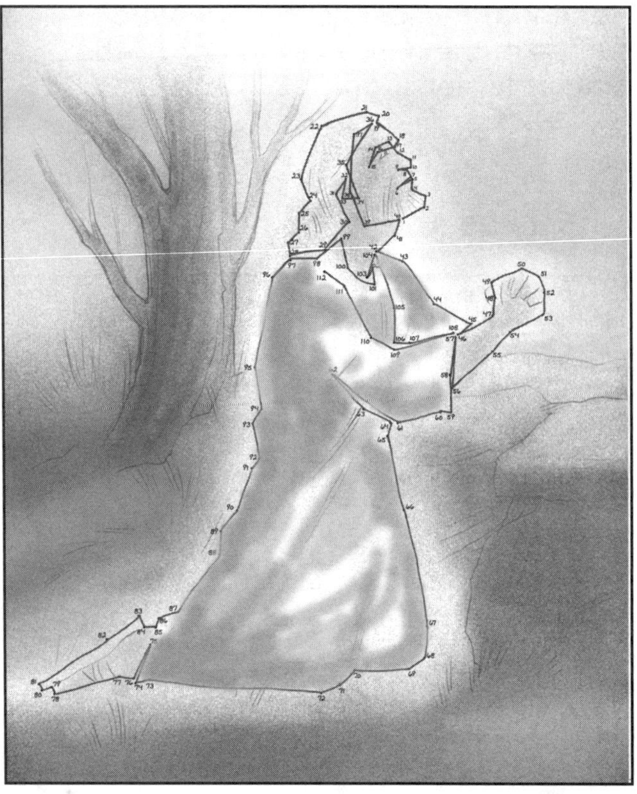

Jesus is praying in the garden.

Activity 37 (p. 57)

Garden is the only one that is not a building.
Orange is the only fruit.
Lemon is the only one that doesn't make sense if preceded by the word blue.
Gloves are for the hands, not the feet.
Open is the opposite of the other three words.
Tuesday is a day, not a month.
He is the only singular pronoun.
Alligator is the one you probably wouldn't give your child as a pet. (It's also the only reptile.)

GOLGOTHA is the answer.

Activity 38 (p. 58)

At the tomb (Luke 24:10): **more than 3** (Mary Magdalene; Joanna; Mary, the mother of James; and the other women with them)

Behind closed doors (John 20:19, 24): **10**—the 12 minus Judas and Thomas (By this time "the 12" was how the disciples were known, but as this was after Judas betrayed Jesus and before a replacement had been found for him, there would have been a total of 11 disciples. However, since Thomas wasn't there for some reason, the answer is 10.)

On the road to Emmaus (Luke 24:13, 18): **2** (Cleopas and another)

Behind closed doors (John 20:26-29): **1** (The 12 disciples minus Judas = 11, but because we can't count the same people twice we have to subtract 10 of these—the 10 who saw him in John 20:19, 24.)

At one time (1 Corinthians 15:6): **more than 500**

Total: more than 3 + 10 + 2 + 1 + more than 500 = **more than 516**

Activity 39 (p. 59)

Feed my sheep.

Activity 40 (pp. 60-61)

Answers will vary.

Activity 41 (p. 62)

Stephen—step, hen (*he* is permissible)
Philip—lip
Prochorus—chorus
Nicanor—can, or
Timon—on
Parmenas—arm, as / men, as
Nicolaus—cola, us

(Note: words like *pro* are not really words by themselves, but are prefixes and sometimes used for short.)

Activity 42 (p. 63)

Paul was an apostle.

Saul's/Paul's name was never changed. *Saul* is a Hebrew name. *Paul* is the Greek version of the same name.

Barnabas defended Saul (Paul) to the disciples.

Paul wasn't trusted at first by the disciples because at first he persecuted Christians. (See paragraph one.)

Paul made three missionary journeys (see paragraph two).

Activity 43 (p. 64)

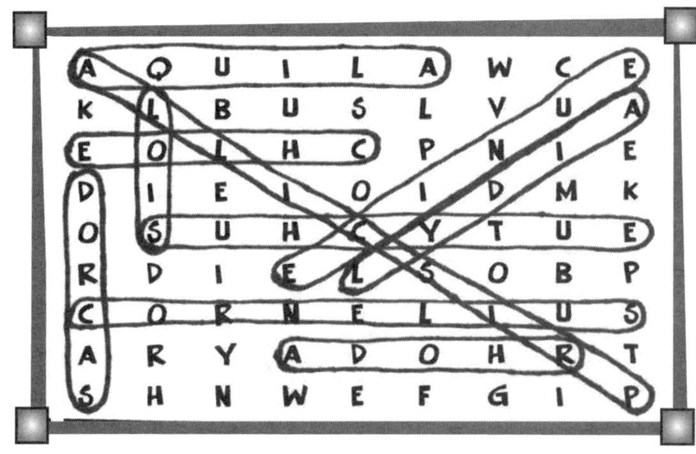

Activity 44 (p. 64)

EUNICE and LOIS (Lystra)
DORCAS (Joppa)
CORNELIUS (Caesarea)
RHODA (Jerusalem)
LYDIA (Thyatira)
PRISCILLA and AQUILA (Rome and Corinth)
EUTYCHUS (Troas)
CHLOE (Corinth)

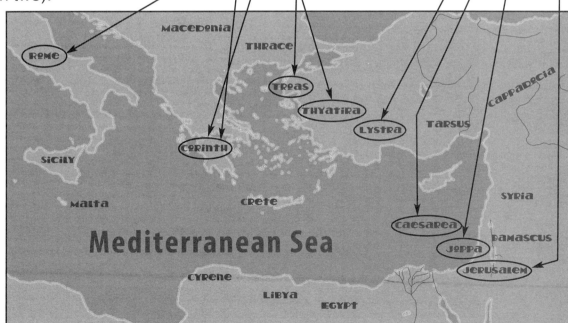

Macedonia
Rome
Thrace
Troas
Thyatira
Cappadocia
Lystra
Tarsus
Corinth
Sicily
Malta
Crete
Syria
Caesarea
Mediterranean Sea
Joppa
Damascus
Jerusalem
Cyrene
Libya
Egypt

Activity 45 (p. 67)

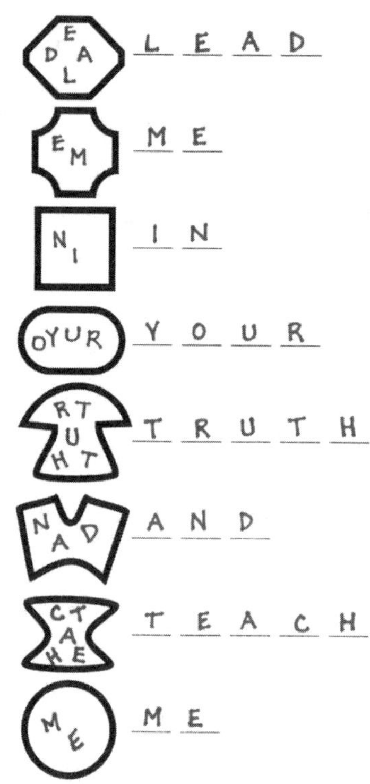

Lead me in your truth and teach me. (Psalm 25:5a)

Activity 46 (pp. 68-70)

The person who helped Paul but was never a close personal friend is Ananias.

Activity 47 (p. 71)

S	*Simon Peter was a disciple of Jesus.*	
E	*Exodus is the second book of the Old Testament.*	
	All people in the world are Christians.	A
T	*Titus is the name of a book in the New Testament.*	
T	*There are 66 books in the Bible.*	
	Numbers is a book in the New Testament.	N
H	*Hallelujah is a word praising God.*	
E	*Ezekiel was a prophet.*	
	Exodus is the book of the Bible that tells about Esther.	E
	X-rays were common in Bible times.	X
	Amos was one of the twelve disciples.	A
B	*Bread is a symbol of communion.*	
E	*Esther was a queen.*	
	Martha was the mother of Jesus.	M
L	*Leviticus is the third book in the Bible.*	
I	*Inviting a lonely friend to church is a good thing to do.*	
E	*Each of the four Gospels is named after a person.*	
	Psalms and Proverbs are New Testament books.	P
V	*V is used in the names of only three books of the Bible.*	
E	*Easter celebrates the resurrection of Jesus.*	
R	*Revelation is the last book of the Bible.*	
	Lucy is the name of one of the four Gospels.	L
S	*Samuel anointed Saul king of Israel.*	
	Esther was the cousin of Moses.	E

Set the believers an example.
(1 Timothy 4:12b)

Activity 48 (pp. 72-73)

THERE IS NO LONGER

JEW OR GREEK,

THERE IS NO LONGER

SLAVE OR FREE,

THERE IS NO LONGER

MALE AND FEMALE;

FOR ALL OF YOU

ARE ONE IN CHRIST JESUS.

GALATIANS 3:28

BROTHERS AND SISTERS,

DO NOT BE WEARY

IN DOING WHAT IS RIGHT.
2 THESSALONIANS 3:13

WHEN YOU ARE OFFERING YOUR GIFT AT THE ALTAR,

IF YOU REMEMBER THAT YOUR BROTHER OR SISTER HAS SOMETHING AGAINST YOU,

LEAVE YOUR GIFT THERE BEFORE THE ALTAR AND GO;

FIRST BE RECONCILED TO YOUR BROTHER OR SISTER,

AND THEN COME AND OFFER YOUR GIFT.
MATTHEW 5:23-24

Activity 49 (p. 74)

I am the **GOLDEN RULE:**

In everything do to others as you would have them do to you. (Matthew 7:12)

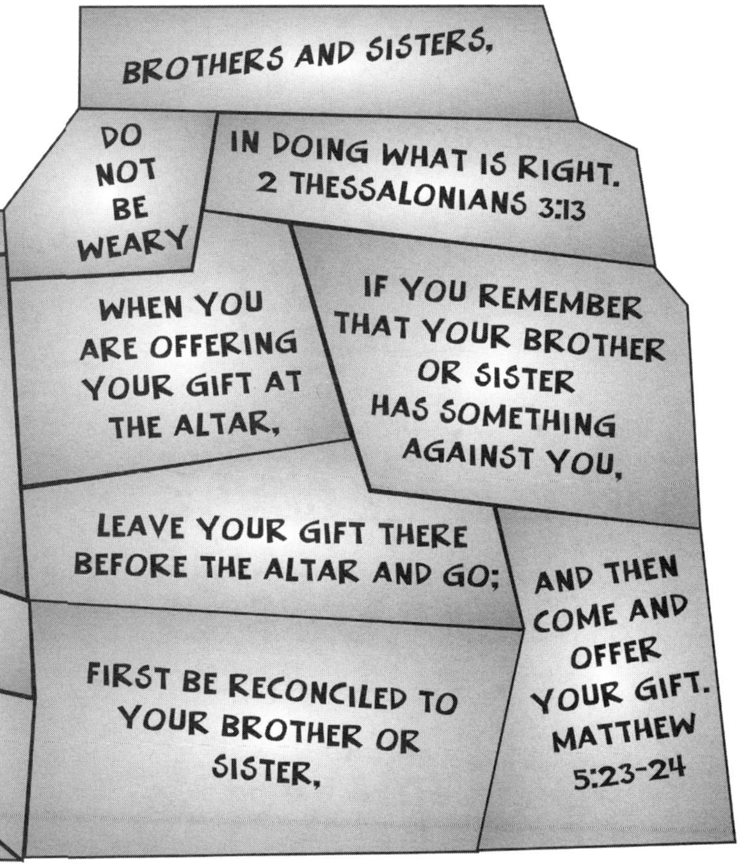

Activity 50 (p. 75)

"You shall love the Lord your God with all your heart, and with all your soul, and with all your mind." This is the greatest and first commandment. (Matthew 22:37-38)

Activity 52 (p. 77)

1. *When you go without anything to eat for a long time and your stomach begins to growl, you are what?* **HUNGRY**
2. *What you need if you're suffering from hint number 1.* **FOOD**
3. *If you wander around in a desert for a long time without water, you become what?* **THIRSTY**
4. *After you eat something really salty you want something to* **DRINK**.
5. *Someone you meet for the first time is a* **STRANGER**
6. *To be hospitable. To make someone feel good when they come to visit you. (past tense)* **WELCOMED**
7. *What you are when you get into a bathtub (besides wet).* **NAKED**
8. *When you get dressed what do you put on? (Use the "ing" form of the word.)* **CLOTHING**
9. *When you don't feel well you are* **SICK**.
10. *When you were a baby someone* **TOOK CARE OF** *you. (3 words)*
11. *If you have committed a serious crime, you will be sent here.* **PRISON**
12. *When you went to see someone at their home, you* **VISITED** *them.*

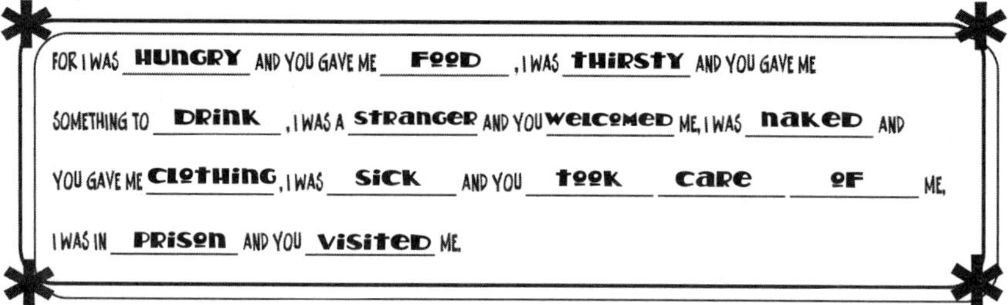

FOR I WAS HUNGRY AND YOU GAVE ME FOOD, I WAS THIRSTY AND YOU GAVE ME
SOMETHING TO DRINK, I WAS A STRANGER AND YOU WELCOMED ME, I WAS NAKED AND
YOU GAVE ME CLOTHING, I WAS SICK AND YOU TOOK CARE OF ME,
I WAS IN PRISON AND YOU VISITED ME.

Activity 51 (p. 76)

Activity 53 (p. 78)

Truly I tell **you**, just as **you did it to** one of the least **of** these who are members **of** my family, **you** did **it to** me.
(Matthew 25:40)

1. it
2. did
3. you
4. of
5. to

Activity 54 (p. 79)

NOW THERE ARE VARIETIES OF GIFTS, BUT THE SAME SPIRIT; AND THERE ARE VARIETIES OF SERVICES, BUT THE SAME LORD; AND THERE ARE VARIETIES OF ACTIVITIES, BUT IT IS THE SAME GOD WHO ACTIVATES ALL OF THEM IN EVERYONE.

Activity 55 (pp. 80-82)

Box 1—THE FRUIT OF THE SPIRIT
faithfulness, generosity,
gentleness, joy, kindness,
love, patience, peace
self-control

Box 2—THE WORKS OF THE FLESH
anger, drunkenness, envy,
idolatry, jealousy, quarrels

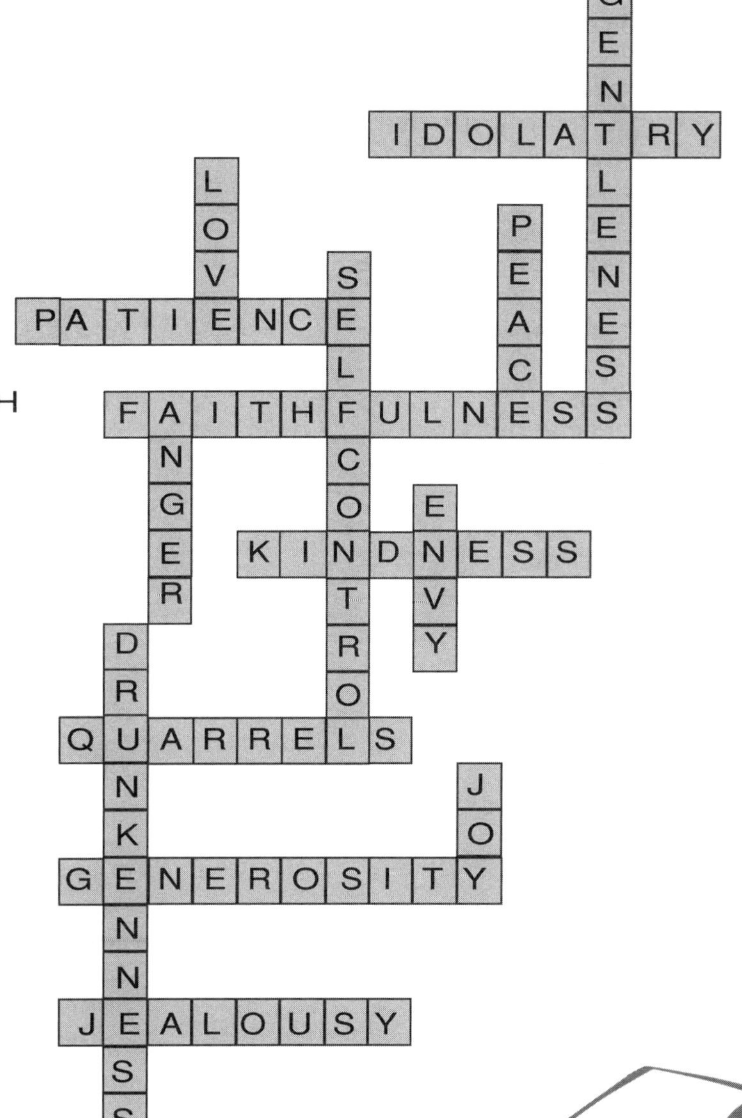

Activity 56 (p. 83)

Any answers you give are correct for you.

Here are our answers:

Psalm 38:1—guilt
Psalm 42:9—lonely, scared
Psalm 43:1a—self- justification
(I'm right—they're wrong)
Psalm 95:1—happy
Psalm 102:7—lonely, alone
Psalm 116:1—happy, satisfied
Psalm 130:5—hopeful, patient
Psalm 133:1—thankful, pleased with life
Psalm 139:7—guilty, annoyed
Psalm 140:1—afraid

Activity 57 (p. 84)

No one answer. Your proverbs must come from your own experiences.

Activity 58 (pp. 85-87)

Letters (in order)	Written by	Written to
Romans	Paul	church at Rome
1 Corinthians	Paul	church at Corinth
2 Corinthians	Paul	church at Corinth
Galatians	Paul	church at Galatia
Ephesians	Paul	church at Ephesus
Philippians	Paul	church at Philippi
Colossians	Paul	church at Colassae
1 Thessalonians	Paul	church at Thessalonica
2 Thessalonians	Paul	church at Thessalonica
1 Timothy	Paul	Timothy
2 Timothy	Paul	Timothy
Titus	Paul	Titus
Philemon	Paul	Philemon
Hebrews	?	?
James	James	the twelve tribes
1 Peter	Peter	Christians
2 Peter	Peter	Christians
1 John	John	a church
2 John	John	a church
3 John	John	a church
Jude	Jude	?

Activity 59 (p. 88)

The circle, triangle, and infinity symbol have no beginning and no end, just like God.

The other symbols are all symbols for the Trinity, having three equal parts

INDEXES

Topic, Activity, AND SCRIPTURE

TOPIC INDEX

GOD CALLS

ANSWERING GOD'S CALL

ISRAELITES RESPOND

BIRTH OF THE SAVIOR

JESUS' MINISTRY BEGINS

JESUS AND THE DISCIPLES

ROAD TO JERUSALEM

UPPER ROOM TO EASTER

DISCIPLES CARRY ON

LIVING GOD'S WORD

DISCIPLESHIP INSTRUCTIONS

LEARNING GOD'S WORD

ACTIVITY INDEX

MYSTERIES

RIDDLES

PUZZLES

TRICK QUESTIONS

MORE

SCRIPTURE INDEX

OLD TESTAMENT

MIXED OLD TESTAMENT

MIXED OLD AND NEW TESTAMENT

NEW TESTAMENT

MIXED NEW TESTAMENT

CREDITS

ART CREDITS

pp. 1, 3, 5, 7–18, 20–27, 29–30, 33–49, 51–65, 67–72, 74–89, 107–112 (background); pp. 2–5, 7–27, 29–49, 51–65, 67–112 (puzzle-piece folio); pp. 7–26, 29–48, 51–64, 67–72, 74–88 (border); p. 29 (all but Advent wreath); p. 36 (gifts); p. 41 (mirror); p. 82 (boxes); p. 88 (infinity symbol): © Shutterstock

p. 7 (animals): Charles Jakubowski, © 2004 Cokesbury

p. 8 (animals): Dennis Jones, © 2005 Cokesbury

p. 9 (ark): Dennis Jones, © 2006 Abingdon Press

pp. 12 (sun/moon/stars, sheaves of wheat), 13 (bread and cake, goblet, fat and lean cows): Mike Meredith, © 2009 Cokesbury

pp. 13 (healthy and withered grains of wheat), 30 (girl and trunk, baby portrait), 31 (baby portraits), 68–69 (portraits): Mike Meredith, © 2010 Cokesbury

p. 17 (Rebekah): Francis Phillips/Linden Artists, © 2004 Cokesbury

p. 17 (Chloe): Christa Hook/Linden Artists, © 2007 Cokesbury

p. 17 (Esther): Francis Phillips/Linden Artists, © 2006 Cokesbury

pp. 17 (Eve), 18 (Sarah): Marcy Ramsey/Portfolio Solutions, © 2008 Cokesbury

p. 18 (Ruth): Cheryl Arnemann/John Walter and Associates, © 1997 Cokesbury

p. 19 (Abraham, Adam, Barak, Boaz, Haman, Isaac): Peter Stevenson/Linden Artists, © 2001 Cokesbury

p. 20 (Saul tangram): Randy Wollenmann, © 2003 Cokesbury

p. 21 (the ark of the covenant): Richard Hook/ Linden Artists, © 2009 Cokesbury

pp. 24 (maze), 56 (dot-to-dot): Randy Wollenmann, © 2010 Cokesbury

p. 26 (animals): Dennis Jones, © 2004 Cokesbury

p. 29 (Advent wreath): Paige Easter, © 2005 Cokesbury

p. 37 (water, shell, descending dove): Florence Davis, © 2001 Cokesbury

pp. 55 (puzzle), 56 (sheep): Paige Easter, © 2006 Cokesbury

p. 64 (map): Randy Wollenmann, © 2008 Cokesbury

p. 76 (puzzle): Paige Easter, © 2007 Cokesbury

p. 88 (triquetra, shamrock, entwined circles): Randy Wollenmann, © 2004 Cokesbury

PHOTO CREDITS

pp. 22, 42: © Shutterstock

p. 48: Ron Benedict, © 2010 Cokesbury